Sexoirs of a Gigolo

COMPLETE COLLECTION

ASH ARMAND, NICK HAWK AND BRADLEY LORDS

Published by Vigliano Books

ISBN-10: 0989330095
ISBN-13: 9780989330091

$\mathscr{I}$NTRODUCTION

My name is Garren James and I am the owner of the largest straight male escort agency in the world. I was contacted by Vigliano Books for a book proposal and I loved the idea so much we included this in one of the Gigolos episodes on Showtime. The publisher tasked each of the gigolos with writing their sexiest story- a "sexoir." I instantly loved the word "sexoir" but was clueless as to what it was. So what is a sexoir? A sexoir is a memoir of your sexual escapades, told in any way that you want. What was your first time like, what was your first escorting job like, what was the craziest, funniest, most romantic… it's anything YOU want it to be.

After graduating from college with a double major and a football scholarship, I was scouted to become an international runway and print model. This brought me into contact with the most alluring men in the world and we always shared notes on what women wanted and desired. Simply put, every woman wants a man who is a perfect gentleman. When I started Cowboys4Angels, I had no clue the amount of success it would have. After extensive research, I found there was no agency in the United States that offered male companionship strictly for women. There were many male escorts catering to men who occasionally catered to women as well. They were labeled in the industry as bi-sexual male escorts. I found that women were very turned off by this, and then it dawned on me why the business of male escorts for women in America had failed so miserably...I can't imagine any woman wanting to hire a man who had just been out with another man! I think women felt as if the men were only into men and were faking the experience they were sharing with women. That's why Cowboys4Angels is an agency offering male companions for women and women alone.

The agency has been a hot topic for the press. I have personally appeared on *the Tyra Banks Show*, *Dr. Phil*, *20/20*, *Nightline News*, *the Joy Behar Show*, NatGeo's *Taboo*, and the list goes on. We have been featured in *Playgirl*, *Glamour*, *Sheen*, *Hustler*, and *Esquire* magazines. But most importantly, we are featured on Showtime's hit series *Gigolos*, which just wrapped up its fifth season. It started out as an idea and it has blossomed into one of Showtime's most watched shows. I get recognized by women all over the country who love the show. I've even had a group of 10 firefighters who were in New York City for a seminar come up to me at the airport in New York and tell me they watch at the station every week! They said they are watching the show looking for tips to improve their romancing skills.

I loved the movie *American Gigolo*, starring Richard Gere, and wanted to make that a reality instead of just a screenplay. In the film Richard Gere's character is a gigolo that is blatantly narcissistic and superficial; however, you can tell he takes pleasure in his work by being able to satisfy women. In the movie, Richard Gere is able to make his clients feel free to discuss their fears and insecurities and honestly discuss the lives in which they are seemingly trapped. Having a group of men that cared about women enough to go out of their way to make a date as romantic as possible was the main idea that I wanted to promote. At the end of that film a client of his comes to the rescue and saves him from being convicted of a crime he didn't commit. His client cared

Garren James being interviewed for
Nightline News **by Juju Chang.**

enough for him to risk her reputation in order to save him from
a lengthy prison sentence. It's obvious that if he hadn't done his
job well and made her feel special enough to come to his rescue,
he would have been locked away for life. That's an incentive to
all the men who work for Cowboys4Angels to always do their
best. They never know the rewards it may bring!

The men I represent need to be at least 21 years old, but I find
that the best ones are between the ages of 25 to 35. They usually
come from professional backgrounds. Not all must be working as
male models. All must be very well-traveled, cultured, educated
and most importantly, be very proficient in making a woman feel
safe and relaxed. The men need to be very attractive, dedicated to

a top level of fitness, presentable, well-groomed, stylish, charming, and desirable. Cowboys need to be confident but not arrogant, somewhat innocent yet savvy. All need to be emotionally mature, stable and possess a genuine respect for women. The men who meet the physical requirements but don't make the cut are usually arrogant or just plain dull. For example, I was once interviewing a prospective escort who told me several times that he had often been approached to sell his sperm due to his superior genetics. He also told me that he was better looking than Brad Pitt. This interview ended shortly after when I realized he would want the clients to worship him instead of the other way around!

Just as Cowboys4Angels has created something new and excitingly different about male escorts for women, this book is now about to create something new and excitingly different about erotic novels. 99% of the time erotic novels are penned by a woman who fantasizes herself in passionate, dream-filled adventures with a handsome, strong, daring man as she sits at her computer in her basement or office. However, the authors of the sexoirs who are featured in this series have a unique perspective far from any woman. These authors are MEN! They are unique in the fact that they have lived the life and have first-hand experience with real life erotica!

I was searching a modeling website when I found Ash Armand. He had a totally different look than anyone I represented at the time and I told myself that I had to have this guy! I called him asked if he would like to set up a meeting. He was very polite on the phone and was a little shocked when I explained who I was. I asked him to just give me a few minutes of his time, and I flew to Miami to meet him. I remember showing his photos to some lady friends and they were all literally drooling. I have had countless men send me photos that have been enhanced to hell. When I meet them, I don't recognize them at all. That's why I must meet all of my men in person before I hire them. Obviously I have to make sure the photos are current and the men are not the rare kind that take amazing photos but have no "stage presence." So what is stage presence? Basically I have to make sure that when they walk into a room, heads will turn. They have to be able to make a woman feel special when she first sees him as he enters to meet her. Ash is one of those men with incredible stage presence. Even before *Gigolos* aired, when I was out with him, people wanted to be close to him to find out who he was. He has a star-like presence that shines from within. When I walked up to him for our first meeting, I was shocked that he was better looking in person than in his photos. I think it was his smile. He radiates this calming friendliness that makes you feel instantly at ease. That's a rare thing when first meeting someone. We started talking about his current profession. He didn't simply tell me that he was a massage therapist. He said he was currently "specializing in the art of massage." He told me he was trained in many body arts from India and the Orient. He also related experience in indigenous folk traditions as well as ultramodern skills from western masters and sensuous edges of science. I wondered what woman would not want an "artistic" massage from this guy. When he was introduced on *Gigolos*, he never looked back and in time became a true professional. He is a physically, mentally, and spiritually active person, and all of his clients love that aspect of him. I have never once had a client tell me she did not enjoy her time with Ash. Clients are always calling me the minute the date is over to schedule another encounter. This proves time and time again that he is one of the best in this industry.

I hope you're ready for what you're about to read because it's a real life account from your very own Gigolo. Let your imagination run wild as you read his story.

Ash Armand

PREFACE

We are born onto this planet with the sense of an inherent yet inexplicable mission, pressuring us with its need to be fulfilled in our current lifetime. For some, their calling naturally surfaces early on. For others, like me, we forage our path in this game we call life. Armed with experience, inspiration, and the desire to be of service, I'm able to piece together the puzzle of insights and moments of high impact, all offering visions and clues. I have known I would be a healer of some sort ever since I was a kid – thanks to my mom and her fascination with Shiatsu and alternative medicines. Strength, vitality, passion, and the miraculous vessel we are blessed to call our bodies have been my most prominent inspirations and women: my constant captivation. It is no wonder the universe has placed me in the role I play today.

My nerves tense and my mind races every time the minutes speed closer to the moment of encounter with a new client and her entourage of mysteries. Expectations and desires grown from a lifetime of culture-fed, family-pruned, emotionally-sown, and experience-laden crops of tended or possibly fermented riddles occurring and soon to be outpouring from the depths of her human existence. To be heard, nurtured, and coddled is every goddess's birthright and a talent with which I've been cosmically endowed. A book all her own and I, in service, offer my time and attention to her details. Each lady may conceal prose upon woes or hales in mystifying tales. Universes to be discovered yet all reflections of the divine Shakti, Yin, or cosmic female energy manifested in human form. Here I present to you a window view of meticulously selected tales depicting experiences along my path which have had the most impact in shaping me into the master of the love I radiate today. The first, 'Ride to the Break of Dawn,' is based on the beginning of my relationship with my love. The second, 'Beyond the Labyrinth,' is based on a steady client encounter. And the third, 'Dreamlandia,' is based on a one-night stand.

Ride to the Break of Dawn

The hours tick-tocked while I waited thinking of her face, her almond eyes, soft flawless skin, and voluptuously inviting lips. An exotic masterpiece I wanted to devour every minute of every hour.

I was captivated by her bold and adventurous nature. She walked right up to me on the dance floor, pressed her delicate yet strong warrior goddess hands on my chest, stood on the tips of her toes, and into my ears her words hissed, "So who the heck are you, anyway?!" I smiled in awe as I brought her closer, my hand on her waist, to pour my name over her neck and into her ear. She turned her face and met mine an inch apart. Time stood still and the rest of the world disappeared. Only she and I remained in all of existence.

She danced like a snake, hypnotizing me with her hips. Magnetized to hers, my body responded in perfect sync. Together we translated the sounds with graceful passion.

The music stopped, she pulled away.

Her smile lingered, eliciting an unspoken welcome. Nevertheless she walked away. I went after her and stole a few words before she could escape again but she did, again and again until I finally cornered her. Looking into her beautiful eyes sparkling under the dim lighting, I nuzzled my face in her hair —drinking her scent. My nose tickled her neck sending ripples of laughter through the air, interweaving our energies, unveiling a deep connection. Seconds later her lips were on mine as I caressed her breasts, pressed against my chest. Right then, I had a deep realization. We've known each other from former worlds, past lives, we have always been intimately connected and now again in this space, in this time.

Months passed and my feelings never ceased nor did they remain the same. They grew with intensity. My body had this insane addicted craving for hers. I ached for her. Beyond the pungent streets, bums and alcohol infested loiterers, I could smell her. As I walked down the cold wet streets of New York City, the memory of her wetness filled me. Entranced by the lingering reminiscent aromas of her vulva, I could taste her sweetness. My insatiable hunger for her blinded me from every other woman. I noticed no one else. *How could this be?* I wondered. *Is this healthy, to be constantly thinking with such insatiable hunger for only her?* With every step that revealed a memory of her, my mouth watered with desire. *Is she a witch?* I pondered. *Has she cast a spell on me?* If so, I begged the universe to never let it be broken. May we continue to mesmerize each other − growing and evolving together, as we share our journey in this lifetime.

How much I yearned to be inside her. Patience. I had to be patient. Cultivating this virtue had never been such a prominent part of my everyday experience as it was then. The hours we were apart were torturous. She thought I would pick her up from work for her safety but it was genuinely for my own pleasure of being with her sooner than later. This particular day had been the most testing day of all because she was working a triple shift covering for co-workers during the Thanksgiving holiday. It was nearly 2 am.

My palms began to bead with sweat as I approached the door to Merchant Restaurant and Cigar Lounge. I swung it open while my heart began to beat like thunder only to be instantly swayed to ease by her ravishing presence. Her flirtatious eyes, seductive lips, nurturing bosom, and immediate embrace made my body scream with gratitude. My lips drank from her essence, her spirit, her love. I fought with the impulse of ripping her clothes off right then and there. How could I survive two more hours with my manhood practically tearing a hole in my pants?! If I did rip off her clothes right there, would anyone object at the sight of such enchanting beauty or would they all gather around in awe and benevolent admiration as I shared the intimate art of loving with slow, delicate passion? I was tempted to find out, when her manager tapped me on the shoulder. I turned to find eyes full of jealousy glaring into mine. "I hate to break this up guys but I'm sure you can find a better place for that. Good night, beautiful. Get her home safe and let her rest. She's had a long day," said the manager. His dry, chapped mouth said one thing but his eyes told another more scornful story.

With my arm wrapped around her shoulders and hers around my waist, we faced the coming dawn. Her voice tickled my ears with sweet words. Yet all I wanted was to silence her with my tongue. I was grateful for the red lights that halted us at every crosswalk as they allowed me a few moments to revel in her embrace.

We stepped down into the desolate underpass. The silence swallowed our words in the still darkness of the subway tunnel. Only lust remained. Nothing more could be spoken; there were no more words to utter. Now the only sounds were of our breathing, the roaring of the train that finally came, and its heavy, musty wind blowing our hair. We stepped in with a kiss.

Our kiss ignited a roaring fire of ravenous passion. Like a vampire, I attempted to suck every ounce of fresh love from her neck. I inhaled it from her every visible pore and I wanted more. I trailed my fingertips over her lips, face, down her neck, and over her nipples. She inhaled me with each breath, caressing my face with hers. Sucking my lips as I awakened her areolas like puckering daisies, I lifted the fabric of her dress to blow a cooling breath over her, then squeezed. She pressed my hands on her breasts. We suddenly became aware of whispers around us, but that only made her giggle as she cleverly abducted and introduced my hand to her super juicy yet hidden treasure garden.

With one leg over my lap, her skirt concealed my adventurous fingers, which had the honor of indulging in such an exquisitely titillating vaginal quest. I teased her, massaging her clitoris, then pulling her lips and pressing the entry. She kissed my neck and removed her coat and laid it over her waist and my lap. Now she began to slowly unbuckle my belt and unbutton my pants. She slipped her cool fingers over my hot member sending a rush of energy up my spine; my entire body began to tingle. My thumb pressed and massaged her clit while my fingers stimulated her g-spot. Her body began to uncontrollably undulate.

In an unexpected instant, she jumped off my lap and stood up against the single door next to our seats. Breathing heavily while biting her lower lip and touching herself, she licked her lips. In another instant, I was up and standing in front of her, pressing my throbbing penis against her womb. I liberated her breasts from her dress. Pressed up against the door, she moaned as I sucked her breasts and caressed her nipples with my tongue. Unable to contain herself, she ripped open my shirt. She kissed me, fervently pressing her breasts onto my bare chest before thrusting me into her place. She removed my belt and unzipped my pants to free my pulsing cock. With one foot on the seat next to us and one hand on the upper rail, she lifted herself and welcomed me into her wet, luscious yoni. I held her voluptuous right thigh as she rotated her hips while pumping her hungry pussy as it sucked on my lingam, squeezing and releasing it with intoxicating momentum. It felt so good inside her warm wetness. She knew just how to move as her pussy sucked and pulled me in, out, and around.

I grabbed hold of her other thigh as she wrapped both arms around my neck, grabbing my hair. I carried her and shifted back down onto the seats. She increased the rhythm as she rode me to our Kingdom of Cum. I slid my hands under her skirt to squeeze her firm, bodacious booty. She continued to dance on me with the most delicious flows of passion. Together we began to shake and spasm with orgasmic ecstasy. I squeezed her body into mine as we melted into bliss. Staring into each other's eyes, I sprinkled feather light kisses over her. Suddenly realizing the train was no longer moving, a pair of hands applauded as the conductor announced over the speaker "final stop." The double doors opened to reveal the light of the breaking dawn.

BEYOND THE LABYRINTH

No longer a novice but instead a full-fledged connoisseur in the industry of companionship, I exit the helicopter of she whom shall remain unnamed. She is not a new client. I have already been initiated into her treasure trove of exotic intricacies. This maiden does not fit into the same category as most clients. She jumps out of the box of norms and creates her own genre. This woman is more like a labyrinth. Each nook and cranny of her deepest mazes exposes a varied personality of her diversified soul. For the purpose of protecting her anonymity, I won't mention how she acquired her wealth or how she multiplied it exponentially over time. Instead allow me to introduce you to an altruistic lair of her kinks and pleasures. As I descend the final step and stand firmly on the perfectly tamed manicured lawn of her Italian villa, I take in the familiar landscape and brace myself for what is to come. Escorted by her prudish yet trusted assistant, she is dressed in a form fitting black silk jumpsuit with a white lace tux flap, velvet blazer and red bow tie. "Buon giorno," she says. And concealing a smile, she rather simply and with a slight hint of coy, bows her head in what must have been her warmest regard. I bow in return and offer my welcoming palm. Awaiting a hand for my lips to kiss in gallant greeting, I am startled into a nervous laughter at the sight of its silent substitute. Her red-leathered fingers place what appear to be lingerie delicately displayed in red lace with golden side ruffles garnished by a glittering elegantly long black feather.

The chauffeur, who is also the esteemed footman, carries my small Louis Vuitton luggage which had been gifted to me by another client.

A gentle Tuscan breeze draws my attention back to that which lay in my palm tickling my nostrils with a seductive scent of ylang ylang, jasmine, and rose combined. I unclasp what I believe is a rose quartz to reveal a beautiful note written in such lovely cursive handwriting on paper resembling ancient papyrus. And this is what it says:

"Welcome, Oh gallant rider of erotic dreams,
The roses have been pruned in your tribute

In the rose laden labyrinth you shall find your royal garment
And so shall commence this eve's entertainment

If you succeed in your pursuit
Two harem maidens will appear as you retrieve your suit
Together they will disrobe you and dissolve your stress and your fear
Under the moonlight they shall bathe you in petals, oils, warm giggles, and cheer

Eventually by the fire we shall dine
& I shall finally pretend your love is mine."

The colors dancing in the sky give proof that dusk is soon approaching. My heart begins to pound knowing far too well the complexity of the rose labyrinth, damned to a nearly impossible escape under the new moon light. Luckily, I have learned quite a bit from these unpredictable escapades. Armed with my comfortable running shoes and trusted high lumens headlamp that I quickly retrieve from my Prada sling, I begin to speed-walk towards the adventure ahead. Once I manage to secure the headlamp firmly and comfortably on my head, I pull my hood and dash with determined speed and graceful precision. I cannot emphasize enough just how grateful I feel for having chosen to wear the well-cushioned stallion stead shoes encasing my feet.

What a beautiful run down the red and black moss patched cobblestone path, swerving between soft, grass covered meadows sprinkled with flowers and naturally adorned with such happily bountiful trees.

I come to a full halting stop when I arrive at the entrance of the ancient labyrinth. A giant pair of marble lions stands guard at each side of the iron goddess gate. I kneel down, bowing my head in reverence while extracting a lighter and a stick of Palo Santo, a Peruvian energy clearing aromatic bark, from my sling. While lighting the stick I whisper this prayer; "I bow in true service tonight to this unbendable manifestation of the Goddess on Earth, may my source-guided intuition steer me on this quest with the force and fierce protection that these giant lions represent and so I take heed responsibly to embody them fully in this now." I am now ready to commence the adventurous ritual ahead.

As I stand up, the goddess' gate opens and I enter like a flash of lighting. The fragrant pathways narrow and fold into dark corners. Although the sun is still accompanying the sky, my top-notch high tech headlamp gets an early start in assisting me through the dark, hidden junctions. Encoded with centuries of lingering pleasures and pains, the vines embed like veins spread across the vintage rustic terrain. The green walls turn with trickery at every illusory bend. I have to calm down, breathe, allow myself to see the way with eyes of the skies. But my thoughts are haunted by the setting sun, the rumble in my hungry belly, and the fatigue in my muscles and bones. I know very well what I need to do but I reluctantly resist, craving food and slumber. Coming upon a glimmering fountain, a voluptuous maiden sculpture pouring water from a grand vase, I can resist no more. I sit on its edge, inhaling deeply the realization that time is a human-bound illusion, the only thing to fear is fear itself and that too is of mental construct without foundation or a worthy verifiable base. So I release both time and fear with a primal exhale, a roar which shatters illusions.

I experience relief at a cellular level, opening inner portals of peace and clarity. An active calming of both spirit and mind dissolves concepts and makes way for deeper truths to blossom with an inner knowing. A deep calmness settles as my love vibration expands, amplifying my senses to what feels like bionic omnipotence.

I rub my hands together rapidly, generating heat, then press my palms over my eyes, down my face, throat, chest, belly, thighs and finally shook them off beyond my knees, bending forward to press my forehead against the refreshing coolness of the fountain's rocky edge. I wet my hands then hydrate my face before standing totally aware of the nearly silent presence of life breathing between the roses. I plunge my hands deeper into the wetness of the flowing fountain reemerging with cupped hands brimming with its sacred waters. With a swift yet agile twirl, I sprinkle the thorn-less roses blooming on the vines.

As the sky begins to bleed orange and red hues from the sun's voyage towards due repose, I sprint swiftly to my target with visceral conviction. I can smell patchouli essential oil and Chanel perfume. Despite the evening's darkness descending, sweet tranquility prevails. Though ignorant to the fact that I am indeed getting closer, I feel a sudden rush of joy as I visualize the moment of accomplishment. A voice lingering in the bush walls alerts a right turn ahead – or was that my own voice? No time to indulge in questions or mysteries. For now, let it be the voice of intuition calling forth destiny. I take the turn so well concealed between walls of soft petal roses. It leads me to another clearing similar to the fountain center except now there stands a statue of lovers: a winged nude male with one hand cradling the head while the other caresses the face of a topless lady with arms embracing him as her dress drapes from her waist to her feet. *Amore e Psiche* reads the marble stone upon which they stand. Cupid and Psyche caught and frozen in time between kisses – no longer intercepted by fear, jealousies, trials, nor judgments. Frozen in an eternal marbleized rapture of freedom in love, it is no surprise Cupid's wing is cast before me as the chosen hook now holding the hanger presenting my suit.

I am startled in this moment by the Chanel-scented naked escort with the fiery red mane, pulling me into a hidden egress leading into an outdoor bathing chamber so inconspicuously masked. Amidst the bubbles and froth of the centrally staged and exquisitely alluring bath simmers a seductress with a golden tress. The maiden with the red mane unhooks the suit from my hand and places it on a standing rack beside a silver framed full-length mirror. She turns around extending her hand. I take it into mine and follow her as she leads me toward the awaiting bath. She begins the ceremony of disrobing me. Placing my bag into another, she continues to peel the sweaty layers sheltering my skin. The voluptuous golden tress seductress steps out of the bath and brings over a chair and step stool just as my pants and briefs are being pulled down below my knees. Placing the chair behind me and the stool in front and slightly to the side, she places her warm palms on my hips, encouraging me to sit as she kneels down beside me tickling my penis with her giggling breath. She trails her fingers down my legs then grabs ahold of one heal to remove the pants, briefs, and sock and then proceeds to free my other leg and foot as well. After she hands the clothes to Miss Red too quickly, she releases my silky hair from the twisted bun encircling the nape of my neck. They lead me to the steps of the grandiose bath.

Golden Tress grabs a crystal glass pitcher with a small circle handle and pours rose scented soap over our bodies. Miss Red giggles, releasing startled moans as the cool liquid slides onto her warm skin. Noticing the small trails on my chest and abdomen they both plunge chin deep to wet their glistening bodies. Standing up once again, they reach for each other, rubbing their bodies together to generate a rich lather. They are almost oblivious to my now full erection. While joined in bubbly pleasure they each extend an arm as an invitation in my direction. I passionately place their arms around my waist creating a circle of foamy delight. Miss Red slithers behind me, scrubbing my back with her breasts; her taut nipples creating electric ripples of highly ecstatic sensations while skillfully massaging and dissolving the soreness from my legs and buttocks. Golden Tress presses her ample breasts against my chest sending strong currents of desire down to the tip of my shaft which she begins to masterfully stroke and pull in perfect rhythm and intensity. My mouth nearly leaps off my face to taste her lips, sucking me in so we are tongue to tongue. Miss Red, armed with a scrubby, washes my entire back side, arms and legs. Golden Tress directs me to sit on a wedged corner of the bath, exposing my erect phallus into the open night air. She kneels down before it and within seconds makes it disappear into her mouth. She pulls down the foreskin, encircling the tip with her tongue, then sucks it so good. I feel the craving to hum into her vagina. Just then Miss Red stands over me, balancing on the top edge of the bath. As she pours water over my head I carry her legs over my shoulders and began to feed on the divinely engorged wetness between her legs. Her soapy hands massage my head as the three of us writhe and convulse with unquenchable, undulating passion. Quivering in shaking climax, I carry Miss Red off my shoulders and into the waters.

Seconds later, Golden Tress mounts me at last and rides me to splashing bliss and surrender. Miss Red joins us by introducing our lips to her hardened nipples. We happily suckle between lustful kisses. Post climactic release, Golden Tress stands up and pulls me to my feet again while Miss Red, eager for her turn to be penetrated begins to rub her supple rear against my happy cock. My fingers travel to greet her wetness, once again bringing my member with eager willingness to enter her tight, luscious garden right there and then. With one hand on her clitoris and the other firmly on her hip I charge right into her wet, vaginal embrace. Golden Tress stands yoni to face with Miss Red, whose mouth does not waste a second diving into her succulent layers. While my hips pump with exalting fervor, Miss Red dines on yoni elixirs and Golden Tress moans into my lips. Nearing climax, I visualize my sacral fire and its fluids rising upward to my heart and crown while contracting my pc muscles. Without restrain, however, my delicious playmates cry in convulsions at the conglomeration of an ecstatic, orgasmic celebration.

"Cleansed with juices of bliss, let us now dress and escort you to our most honorable miss," they chant in unison after our concluding embrace. They pour one final pitcher of flower-scented warm water over me upon exiting the bath and dry me quite diligently before anointing me with essential oils and herbal balms. They press their bodies against me as if to saturate them and rid mine of the excess moisture. The serpentine undulations with which they press have my mouth watering and my penis dripping with longing. They are about to start dressing me with my briefs when they notice my engorged phallus and Miss Red says, "Well we cannot encase him like this." Golden Tress flashes a seductive smile in agreement and together they pamper my penis and scrotum, sucking, pulling, humming, and blowing beyond the borders of maddening ecstasy. What seems like an eternity later, I uncork, gushing a lush froth that they catch and guzzle like the most luxuriant and well-aged champagne, drinking with festive triumph. "I could spend days with these two," I think. While alas that's not possible, the hope of one day having my own harem brings a smile back to shine radiantly upon my face.

They wipe me off and then turn to cleanse their faces while I start to put on the previously ignored fresh silk briefs. Just then, the ladies rush over and signal me to sit. I immediately oblige. In unrehearsed yet perfectly paralleled unison they cradle each foot and began to rub them with the same minty balm sending tingles running up my spine as if zapped with coursing electricity. They conclude what I attribute to be one of the most grounding, honoring foot rituals with the wrapping of each foot in a warm towel and a soft kiss atop the dorsal surfaces. They sock my feet, place them into the legs of the royal trousers and land them comfortably in a pair of handcrafted genuine Italian leather shoes. As I stand they softly pulled up the trousers fastening the zipper, buttons and belt buckle in lovely harmony. Their synchronicity is rather sends me into a trance as their fingers dance in hypnotic collaboration. Before I know it the form-fitting designer shirt is fastened under the embroidered tail coat. They weave my hair into a braid, blow it dry, then release my satin soft locks and don a top hat upon my head. As if lip gloss were icing and my face the cake they comb my eyebrows then gloss my lips and stand back in admiration and awe of their work.

Miss Red hurries over to a trunk from which she unearths a peculiar box. Golden Tress removes the lid to reveal the most delicately fine-spun velvet black cloth. They pull it out and close the box and quite lovingly blindfold my eyes. Suddenly enveloped in darkness and groomed to perfection I feel like an object, a prized possession or like someone's exotic living doll. Definitely not made of plastic but quite possibly in a most honorable miss's mind, heart, and spirit, I am perceived as synonymous with a tool, as a key is to a door. In her experience, I am most often personify the magic formula that initiates the enactment of fantasies conceived in supreme yearning. Birthed in the passionate embrace of persuasive abandon, manipulated by her ingenious resourcefulness, her fantasies are ultimately fabricated in a mutually consensual, spontaneous play of energies. This game is thus justified under the tough hide of my lion heart conscience and liberated from the plagues of the shame that festers from the molding of right and wrong perspectives.

Free from illusory philosophical chains, I release this tangent and resume the scene.

Primped and prepped much too finely to welcome much less entertain fear, I follow the consorts with blinded ease as they begin to lead me on the secret trail to dinner. Flooded in tender waves of tranquil trust they cleverly steer every step, crossing, and passage. Although we are walking it feels like I am floating.

First I hear an obnoxiously piercing screeching; seconds later a soft slender hand takes my left hand while a more assertive hand shocks me with the delivery of an encouraging spank on my butt, rushing me forward a few feet. "Careful now yummy man, you're going to go down, one careful step at a time. Don't worry it's not difficult, we will guide the way," she says. Tempted to peek at the steps, I make a swift attempt to lift the velvet from my eyes. Firm, agile hands briskly intercept and command the velvet to remain in place. "No peeking, love. There's no danger, just trust. Pretend you're on a magic carpet and we're steering the wind." But how could I entertain such imaginings when my feet had to land firmly on each narrow step down this abysmal tunnel? We spiral down what feels like a damp passageway which morphs into a wide inclined corridor. I stop walking with a sigh, exhaling relief. "Darling, are you alright?" I turn toward the voice and yank the velvet off my face, suddenly flooded with the sight of magnificent frescoes, pillars, breathtaking arched windows, terra cotta floors and even a dome. How I got here I'm not meant to know but now that I can see it I do not want to leave. I could spend days exploring every crevice in these splendid quarters, marveling over each detail of artistry. Hanging vines, flowers, and orchids – charmed pillars, walls, windows, and corners.

"We must keep moving, dear knight of lust and passion; your dinner and grand hostess await you," implores Golden Tress. She unties the velvet cloth and places it back in the box with a pair of cuffs which have been ignored. Miss Red joins her in smoothing my edges before pressing their breasts up against my tailored shirt. One hand greets my cock while another pulls my neck lower to facilitate a three-way kiss. I suckle their breasts and press my fingers on their g-spots while my palms massage their clitorises till they soar in undulating ecstasy. I am rock hard and ready as they both drop down to their knees for another gratifying fellatio.

They smooth me out and douse me with more essential oil fragrance. We walk in unison with a lingering aroma of lustful salvation. Limber from sensual rapture and with a comfort in our bodies, we waltz past the adjoining halls and corridors with such buoyant grace and agility as if floating through space. And then, as if the record playing the melodies of our bliss was suddenly scratched to a stop, we are teleported back to our duties by the presence of two enormous doors separating realities and energies.

We take our places, and with deep breaths we brace ourselves for all the unbeknownst events to come. Fully aware that we may never indulge in each other's embrace again, we squeeze one another. I kiss each of their hands and whisper sweet gratitude before pressing them to my heart and my groin. With a little chuckle and a couple of giggles we shake off the remnants of our shared bliss.

I push the doors open with a forceful nudge revealing a Moroccan influenced boudoir. Shimmering fabrics grace the windows, pillows, and settees while candles glimmer in silver lanterns sending beautiful patterns dancing on the walls tickling my fancy and delighting my sore eyes. A lavish buffet of mouthwatering organic gourmet cuisine spreads over an iron-laced, intricately crafted table. Though long it stands low and is decadently dressed and decorated, surrounded by plush pillows and placed over sheepskin carpets. There is a round, king sized bed with a glittering canopy beneath a dome from where one could see the stars sparkling and the new moon hiding. Under high beamed ceilings, there are enormous windows that shelter an immaculate bathing sanctuary. Just beyond the bed, circling back into the great room, is an enchanting high cathedral ceiling from which hangs all kinds of toys and contraptions – silks, swings, ropes, nets and some aerial equipment whose names elude me. On the massive brick and rock wall there is a large metal X with cuffs on the wall beside it. Alongside hooks bearing whips and floggers stand shelves holding electric nails and voltage boxes, strap-ons, and assorted dildos. There are a couple of cages – one hanging and another on the floor just below it with two bronze keys beside it shining in the glowing flames of the flickering fireplace behind them. The massive fireplace held an altar on its mantle, upon which sacred tools, talismans, stones, crystals, statues of deities, oils and tinctures are meticulously displayed. Before the fireplace is a lounge area with the most exquisite fusion of Victorian and Asian-inspired assorted seating. Seeing as the lady of the palace is nowhere in sight, I think it would be wise to have my back to the food and face the fire instead, lest I go mad and burst my capacity for patience. So I opt to sit near the fire perusing the various hanging contraptions.

Red and Golden float in after me in utter silence. They walk up to the fire, light sage, and smudge each other using a beautiful pheasant feather. Then they bow towards each other, interlacing palms over each other's hearts with their foreheads touching and chant a mantra. After the soothing vibrations of their chant become one with the silent space around us, they walk over to the cages. Golden picks up one of the bronze keys and opens the latch of the cage resting on the floor. After handing Red the key she steps inside onto the soft snuggly blankets and pillows. Red locks the latch and hands her the key before walking over to the rock wall and pulling a lever that raises Golden and lowers the other cage. She then proceeds to climb in and lock herself in as well. Golden's slightly heavier weight keeps them both balanced in the air. Now sitting in full lotus, I watch as they progressively enter a deep state of meditation, eventually propelling me into my own inner silent quest.

I half-close my eyes looking at the fire beyond the center tip of my nose whilst commencing pranayama techniques. Just as I am beginning to clear my energy centers, waves of Progressive House music floods my eardrums, startling me to my feet. I freeze at the sight of the veiled mistress in flowing white. She glides right up to me and we stand veil to face. I take off the top hat and bow in charmed respect, welcoming her hand into mine, which she immediately obliges with a curtsy. She begins to twirl an impressive sequence of turns that sends her skirts unfurling in perfect splendid spirals. She lifts the veil while twirling till it is high above her head and then just as gracefully down to her shoulders, as she slows to a stop, winks and blows out a kiss.

"Welcome home, beloved rider of dreams, how I've missed beholding the genuine, sweet compassion your eyes speak. I trust your return was all but dull, huh? Entertaining, at least?"

"Entertaining indeed, most honorable miss," I reply with a charmed smile as I remember the adventure. Her eyes and lips begin gushing giggles of fun, frisky mischief.

"I thought you would appreciate some playtime with my newest and most treasured lovers, Ginger and Cayenne, my sweetest stars by far! Come, let us dine. Please pour me a goblet of wine, dear," she continues. As I hand her a full goblet of her own finest wine, I wrestle with the arranging of a question.

"What do you gain? Or better yet, why go to such elaborate lengths of orchestrating such a masterpiece of sensual delight that you don't see or experience?"

She chuckles and sneers, "Oh so you didn't much care for the adventure and suspense this time around?"

"The suspense and adventure we both know I am used to and am quite adept at grounding in and adjusting to, but this is the first time you grace me with playmates whom just happen to be hanging in cages from your ceiling as we speak. I guess I'm curious to know about your motivation. What inspired today's bathing ritual, grooming ceremony, and blindfolded escort?"

"I strongly feel we can alter our reality. We have the power to manifest our visions and this gives me an opportunity to exercise that power in the role of creator. As a woman, at least half a century young, I have studied, researched, explored and witnessed the consequences of patriarchy and our current systems. Instead of complaining about all the bullshit, I want to find ways to eradicate them by creating solutions. That's my ultimate motivation. On the other hand, today's inspiration stems from a totally selfless realization manifested as an experiment birthed in deep meditation: give Love love and what happens? Can Love love without attachment? The three of you are personifications of pure incarnated Love, embodied on all levels of your existence, and you embrace a selfless servitude offering your time and undivided vibration to those of us who seem either dried up or energetically deprived of such healing frequency. So I decided to show my gratitude and subsequently set the pace with your attraction and passionate cleansing as an opening ceremony and precursor to our erotic play. You must be starving, please sit and make yourself at home" she welcomes.

I begin to unlace my shoes, but I'm suddenly intercepted by her wise fingers as she manages to liberate my anguished feet from the barely broken in shoes. She grants them tender squeezes and caresses the cramps away as my stomach growls impatiently. She stands up, grabs my hands and pulls me up and over to the buffet. "Sit and feast, beloved king of pleasures, treasures, and light!" She rushes over to the hanging cages and moments later we are all wining and dining by the candlelight.

Satiated into a slight food coma, I sprawl out atop the plush bed with a smile as the ladies dance and twirl like fairies in a ring around me. Under the sparkling stars shining through the dome commences the unveiling of the goddess. Ginger and Cayenne begin to peel off the layers of fine silks, lace, and sequined fabrics. They uncover an elegantly aged face which radiates wisdom. Her face features eyes adorned by smile lines – evidence of a life lived fully. There is also a hint of triumph over struggle. Every seductive whirl reveals more pampered skin, but also skin that shelters a lonely heart. She is starving for true love and soul mate companionship, but also overflowing with a potent eroticism. Sliding the veil below her heart exposes a pair of perfectly sculpted breasts. Ginger sends the remainder of her skirts cascading down her hips and beyond her totally shaven yoni.

"Carry me to the X. I want to be bolted, opened, teased, and taunted....Now...Please," she sings entrancingly. I dash to her call without delay, lifting her into my arms and pirouetting my way to the X structure. Cayenne and Ginger stretch open her arms and secure them in the straps with long flowing strokes of love. In one swift instant, I passionately spread her legs, also secured in place.

The hours vanish as we anoint her with oils, teasing and taunting her sprouted nipples. We explore her aged skin, awakening her secret erogenous zones. Cayenne cools her clitoris with ice, I tickle her with feathers, and Ginger punishes her lovingly with an artistic dance of floggers. Her wishes are granted with an elaborate symphony of sucking, teasing, and eventually fucking her beyond desire into a deep, blissful void. Eventually she hangs limp, drained of desire, so we release her and I carry her to her plush throne. She falls into a deep slumber as her eyes flutter with lucid dreams. We cuddle around her and follow her into sleep.

Shocked into waking by a masculine tug at my arm, I open my eyes to behold the footman alerting me of my scheduled departure. I nod in response with gratitude and rather stealthily slither my way out of the tangled bodies. I quickly gather my belongings. I kiss the foreheads of my three sleeping beauties and place a rose in each of their palms. I quietly make my exit, silently closing the grand doors behind me. I run down the corridor, turning back around sharply in hopes of catching a glimpse of the secret door we used the night before. There's no sign of it, a mystery that lingers in my thoughts perhaps to be revealed on another rendezvous. As I step out into the new day I find the footman waiting with an open door to the backseat of a Maserati.

Flashes of what I had just experienced make me tingle with appreciation for portal of bliss we had manifested. Indulgence personified. With two fingers over my lips I blow a kiss their way, Grazie e Prego!

DREAMLANDIA

As if slipping into a virtual world, my body surged with excitement and an uncanny determination to reach corners of Earth still undiscovered by me. The rocks and soil of this place knew my ethereal cosmic name, shouting it in silent vibrations. It felt like an electrifying beckoning only I could hear. As a passenger in my own physical frame, I observed the communication between this indefinable energy and the form I inhabited. In mere seconds and with effortless grace, I was showered, oiled with sandalwood, and dressed to resemble a protector of the forests, mountains, and rivers. For the first time since my recent move, I made no attempts at utilizing the GPS application on my cell phone and instead I drove with a newfound precision and total knowing. I snaked through unfamiliar hills and unnamed passages curving in, out, and through enchanting landscapes before stationing the vehicle off the rocky road beside a cavernous wall.

As I stood beside the closed door of the sleek Camaro, I allowed my eyes to feast on the view of mountain guardians, ocean poetry, and endlessly inspiring skies. The scents emanating from the flowers and the trees joined forces with the lingering energy directing each of my footsteps beyond the cavernous wall to find a naturally concealed path. I began the challenging descent into a valley of enchanting mystery.

Steep, rocky, dusty and dry, laced with a seductively caressing breeze and the entrancing aromas of Jeffrey Pines, White Evening Primrose, Nightshade and Muck Sage all together pleased my senses as I trekked through the rough terrain. My muscles pumped and my heart was charged with endorphins, rapidly circulating ripples of adrenaline through my nerve fibers. The path narrowed deeper into the valley, carving a delicate serpentine arrow across the mountain. Sweat beads crowned my forehead, bubbled throughout every pore, and dampened my threads. The fire within me ignited and burned as I accomplished the most arduous lot of the trek. I vividly remember every stone, crack, and crevice along the path. Climbing down into lush undergrowth, I was welcomed by a great brother eagle soaring above, crying a song of love I recognized as my own – an echo of my timeless soul.

This love song enveloped me and seemed to contain all of existence. Every breath I inhaled quenched my thirsty lungs and with every release I exhaled satisfaction and awe. This love was so deep and so pure, knowing and not knowing, feeling and believing, trusting, guiding and nurturing, and free to simply be. As a wild animal, I carried my muscled body across dry and crumbling rock walls, yet all I felt was a truth beyond humbling. As l looked upon the great wall I had just descended, I realized every moment of this journey is an eternal treasure. I bowed to this great teacher and slowly backed away with my palms pressed together over my third eye in a prayer of reverence and gratitude.

I discovered as I turned around an ethereal virgin goddess of grounds. Earth untouched, unfound! A rainbow of flowers laid claim over plush grasses and mosses unkempt. Birds chirped, butterflies fluttered, and the breeze tickled my skin. The river flirted with me – an attempt at luring me into its luscious depths. Its crystal waters sparkled in the glorious rays of the sun. The river and I would become one. As if floating, I somehow made my way to her mossy edge. I peeled of the sweat soaked fabrics, dipped them into the water, and wrung out every drop before hanging them on an awaiting branch.

In silence, I sat before a majestic cascading waterfall. Unsheathed, I breathed in unison with the rhythm of the falls. For a moment, I thought ants were launching an expedition upon my legs but in immediate answer to my wonderings the feeling intensified tenfold. I opened my palms to receiving and a strong vibration ensued. Heat emanated from my palms, my chest, heart, throat, third eye, and crown. I actually felt my chakras spinning. Energy centers in my body began spinning like vortexes opening portals which had been dormant for so long! What happened next was beyond me, manifesting through me and yet out of my control.

Words can only hinder the experience. I will try to explain the inexplicable but I beg of you, dear soul, if upon your heart you wear thorns that keep you from feeling warmth and passion directly from source: read no further. If the tracks upon your spirit mark trajectories that fester in new world delusions, and if these delusions dictate all that which you robotically obey, or if you are sentenced to a life of discontent, over-consumption, and decaying compassions, you will find yourself buried beneath bricks of judgment that will barricade all other possible realms of reality. However, if beneath your numbness thrives the hope of freedom with a lingering memory of past life blessings, the will of all souls who feel there is more, I invite you to lay down your arms. There is nothing to defend against, no one to judge you. Allow me to dissolve the layers that cloak you. Stand naked with me as I bathe you and soak you in a sweet shower of this most cherished present. May my words caress your heart and make divine love to your spirit. You are already the most magnificently glorious entity.

Roots interlaced my thighs and in an instant an intensely grounding energy penetrated my root center. I began to undulate, thrusting my chest forward. My mouth opened, releasing electric vibrations which pulsated through me in the most melodious tones I have ever been able to resonate and have never since been able to replicate. I began to chant in the language of all ascended beings. I felt as if I were expanding – was I really? I began to slowly open my eyes and I could see colorful lines of energy streaming into my palms, springing from the moss, rocks, trees and even my knees! I was astonished to see spinning wheels over my energetic centers and all around me. With every breath I was blessed. I began a primal dance with the wind and landed again against the mossy earth. I laid my belly flat upon the earth and I felt the pulsing of another heartbeat. I hummed along with the pulsing heart and was suddenly and rather startling rewarded with a lustful moan. The moss softened even further and the silky grasses kissed my skin. As I rolled over, Earth massaged my back, embraced my spirit, and stroked my manhood. My pillar responded with beaming light which caused the grasses to part as the waters of the river pulled me closer. I undulated as I heaved forward while pressing my member into the soothing cool moss, crawling my way toward the rocks. I stood on the cold rocks feeling empowered by nature's passions and was silently greeted by a water nymph.

She grabbed my hand inviting me in. I followed, but when I attempted to return her grasp only waters through my hold would pass. I could see her, an aqueous goddess – an almost translucent sculpture – but alive and captivating. I let go of the desire to touch her and made a conscious choice to revel in this magnetizing manifestation. She poured herself over me, her waters enveloped my body with effervescent wetness. She lathered my chest, neck, and lips with splashes of bliss. In her embrace my scars vanished, my aches evaporated, and my spirit soared. She anointed my phallus, guzzling me with hydrodynamic force and benevolent fury. I could no longer maintain my abstinence as I urged to consecrate this divinely luscious creature with insurmountable passion. As if in answer to my longing, she transfigured magically before my eyes into solid human form. Her crystal eyes gleamed into mine as the river and sky vanished into white.

As I peered into her eyes I noticed their hue slowly fading into a grayish color along with her features, *Wait, you're no Naiad, this is not real, I know this woman*, I thought. *No way, is this a dream? This IS a dream! You're my weekend appointment....* In an instant, I was startled and awake in my own bed again. *Wow, what the fuck?! Really?! Aw man, that felt so real! Who's to say it wasn't? I lived that, all of it, in a dream, yes, I know but it was so lucid and, and, ugh!*

Overwhelmed with disbelief and frustration, I looked over beside me, to find her laying there in the light of the sun that poured through the windows, the face which blasted my awareness into now. How precious and purely angelic to inspire me into such a dream of majestic exaltation.

With a lingering lust coursing through me, I quickly tiptoed to the bathroom, brushed my teeth, rinsed my face, and crept back to the bed – propping myself alongside her. I traced my fingers lightly over her face, outlining her delicate features. She opened her eyes slowly and shined a seductive smile upon me. Instantaneously, she flipped me onto my back and straddled me. Turning her head from side to side, she feathered my skin with a silky silver curtain of hair, sending erotic tingles over my face, neck, chest, belly, lingam, thighs, legs, and feet. Like a dove she flew to the bathroom to freshen and fluff and then stood before me in her celestial buff.

I sat up and welcomed her into my arms. She mounted me effortlessly with long legs hugging my hips as I pulled her closer to devour her ambrosial lips. Her soft succulent breasts pressed against my chest igniting my loins. Breathing in her flowery scent, I grabbed a firm hold of her toned left glute and cradled her head as I delicately spread her reverently across the plush down comforter. Insatiably driven, my tongue trailed across her skin, her hardened pink nipples, and tasted her salty sweat. As I drew near to her parted legs, her hips lifted uncontrollably, it seemed, in wild offering of her blooming pink lotus. She exuded an alluring fragrance and discharged delectable wet nectars.

I lifted her little pink hood, exposing a swollen clitoris, and began to lick her pearl of pleasure. Within minutes she began to writhe and spasm in erotic delusion, grabbing my hair and pressing my head as if to bury it in her yoni. Realizing my tongue was no longer enough, I immediately rose and plunged into her, riding her waves to her bliss and her cum. Deep in orgasmic ecstasy and fueled by her relentless desire to feel me erupt inside her, she manipulated my body into switching places once again. As if I were her Pegasus, she continued to ride me into a long awaited rapture of exalting release. Intoxicated by euphoria, she melted into my arms and together we drifted off into another gratifying adventure in Dreamlandia.

NICK HAWK

$\mathcal{P}$ART 1 - LAS VEGAS

When I first moved to Las Vegas I moved into what I didn't know at the time was the high-rise condo building where the majority of the strippers and escorts lived. I must say I wasn't disappointed in my find. I had been stripping for a few years, and was becoming a well-known gigolo, so finding a mate outside of the "industry" wasn't easy going. I was rather impressed with the talent my new building had to offer. I was in a new town, starting over by myself, and seeing beautiful women running around made it a little less lonely. I ended up getting a very large condo close to the top of the building with a spectacular view of downtown Las Vegas and the surrounding mountains.

On the first floor of the building was a 24-hour gym, where I spent a lot of time breaking a sweat (6 days a week, baby!). It was there that I met Jaslene. She wasn't the typical girl that would usually catch my attention. I'm an alpha male, and generally go for girly girls. Blonde hair, blue eyes, and I've always had a fetish for large breasts. This girl was none of those things, but there was something about her that kept making me glance back.

When I first noticed Jaslene, she was doing lunges with tiny, pink, five pound weights. Very slowly, very methodically. She had long, brunette, luscious hair, which she let flow freely instead of keeping it tied back during her workout. Best of all, each time she stretched out her leg and lunged down, I got a view of an ass I would pay to grab. Every time she started lunging again I'd fake my set of bicep curls and stare at her, imagining what I'd do to her. When she would finish her set, I'd turn away and start doing my own workout, not wanting to seem like a creeper.

Now, most people who know me know that I'm pretty proactive when it comes to the pursuit of a woman. I'm confident in what I bring to the table. When I see what I want, I go for it. But something about this girl was different and kept me from making the move.

I kept eyeing her up and down when she wasn't looking until finally...we locked eyes. The dumbbell I had been curling froze in mid rep, making my right bicep bulge. Her eyes were an intensely deep, almost alien green (mine, in case you're wondering, are hazel). I typically like a little eye foreplay before I make a move and now I was getting it and it was intense. It sounds corny but in that moment I felt like I could see into her soul, her aura emanating from inside her, an emerald green the same color as her eyes. My bicep started to quiver and burn from holding the dumbbell and my eyes broke away. I went to the side of the room to put the weight away, contemplating what I'd say to this mystery woman with the green eyes. For the first time in my life I actually felt tongue tied! I put down the weight in its rack and turned to face her...but she was gone. I missed my opportunity and that doesn't happen often. There was definitely something about this girl...

Over the next few weeks I saw the mystery woman with the green eyes and beautiful ass sporadically. Once I saw her at a trendy Japanese restaurant a few blocks from our building, but I was on a date with a client. This is the first time I even considered talking to another girl while on a date but I couldn't think of a reason and I would never want to hurt a client's feelings.

After that I almost ran her over as I was exiting the parking garage. There she stood, right in front of my car. We locked eyes and she smiled. I didn't know what to say! The car behind me honked impatiently and my mystery woman vanished. I thought to myself, *I'll get her next time.*

Then one night, I was in my condo getting dressed for a workout, when I got a knock on my door. This was the first time anyone had knocked on that door. You need security to enter the premises and I didn't know anyone there. I thought it may have been a neighbor to yell at me about my music the night before. It was actually my mystery woman. She said nothing, handed me a note, smiled and left.

"Dear Venom,

I don't know if I can take being around you for too long without attacking you and jumping on your cock. I have never been this forward with a man I've desired and I have never desired a man as much as I do you. I somehow knew after watching your show we would meet someday. If you are interested in me at all please let know. Preferably sooner than later.

Jaslene (And her number)

PS: You can put it anywhere."

This was possibly the most I have ever been turned on in my life...

PART 2 - RIDING AN ORGASMIC WAVE

Needless to say, my mystery woman got a phone call that night. She lived three floors below me in my building. I invited her to hang out at my place and an hour late she arrived carrying a bag and asked if we could take a bath. I like baths. Especially with naked girls in them. Why not? In her bag she had bath salts, oils, and candles. I was impressed. Typically I would want to get to know someone a little better before getting naked with them but I decided to roll with what was happening. For some reason it just felt right.

After starting the bath and lighting some candles, she had no problem taking her clothes off in front of me. Jaslene's a fucking ten. I'm very turned on at this point, half hard. I must say I enjoy the "chase" somewhat and I'm not typically attracted to girls throwing themselves at me but she definitely had my attention. I'm quite comfortable in the nude as well and my clothes went flying off just as quickly. I'm turned on and amused at the same time. I very much enjoy being turned on and amused.

We both knew what was about to happen so there wasn't much need for any conversation. It didn't take long for us to have our hands all over each other and for me to penetrate her. We reached for each other simultaneously and held each other tight. Jaslene straddled my legs and it felt like a perfect fit. She radiated sex and we were in sexual ecstasy with our arms wrapped around each other. We both took long and deep thrusts. Our lips were locked from the beginning until we couldn't just breathe from our noses anymore. From grabbing each other's backs to the back or our necks, chests, and bottoms we were in unison as we flowed through our liberating motions. The bath water didn't splash over but gave extra sensation. The candles flickered and danced for us as we entered an erotic trance. The wind from my cracked patio door circulated my bathroom. Everything was perfect: the temperature of the air, water, our state of being, that exact time and moment.

I stood up effortlessly and she wrapped her legs around the top of my thighs. We proceeded to my bed and stayed intact as I lay her down. We were in complete control, were limitless and free. The outside world dissipated more with every thrust. Our sexual energy filled the entire room with bursts of almost visual waves. Time stood still, nothing else mattered. Life made sense; we had purpose and we became one. We rode an orgasm like surfers riding a wave and I lost control inside of her as we slowly came back to reality. I looked into her big green eyes and knew she had just experienced the same intensity I had.

No words needed to be said. I believe the best moments in life don't need them. And when you find true understanding in someone, your eyes will say everything. I rolled over and laid on my bed as Jaslene dried off, put her clothes on, and blew out the candles. She then blew me a kiss and floated away. I wouldn't have minded if she stayed but I don't think either of us wanted to ruin the moment and we had to figure out what had just happened. Was this a dream or what the hell had I been missing out on?

A few months had passed and I was really hoping to get another note from Jaslene or at least run into her after she ignored the few texts I sent to her. I'm happy for the experience but now it's honestly not making me feel that great about myself. I'm thinking I finally met someone who I've connected with on a high level and she doesn't want to see me again – possibly because of my profession. I've never connected with someone like that before without dropping molly or ecstasy.

Almost four months later, a note slid under my door. I was really hoping it wasn't another water shut off notice. It read:

"Dear Venom,

I would first like to say that night was possibly the most amazing night I've ever had with someone. I just wanted to fuck you and didn't plan on what happened. I hope you felt something similar to what I felt. It's been really hard and took a lot of restraint not to contact you but I think it would've been harder if I did.

I was really hoping the next time we spoke I would be well and we could run off into the sunset, even if it was for another night. But I'm sorry to write that this is not the case. I didn't want to make you worry about me or involve someone in my life, if my life was just going to be for a short period of time. I was hoping after this last treatment I would be much healthier but it didn't work that well.

I'm a 9/11 survivor and was buried at ground zero, unconscious for many hours. During that time, I breathed in large amounts of asbestos and now suffer from mesothelioma. I have always taken great care of myself and have been living okay for some time now but it's really starting to affect my life and it's really hard.

I don't know how much time I have and the doctors are telling me it may not be much. I hate telling you all of this but if we see each other again I don't think it would be fair for me to hold this from you.

I really want to get to know you but I don't want to put any pressure on you and I don't want to be selfish so please don't pity me or feel obligated to see me again if that night wasn't special for you. But with that said, I would love to take you on a trip. Please text me again if you would like to see me again. If not, I understand and it's totally fine. Let me know what dates would work for you and I will pay for it all. And if it's okay with you, it's always been my dream to go to Costa Rica. If we go, I do ask that you let me live and be free.

Jaslene

PS: The sooner the better.

This was some crazy news and not what I expected to read at all. Many thoughts and confusion clouded my head but honestly I didn't think twice about going on this trip with her. I usually would overanalyze the situation but I decided to just go with it and try not to think. She's teaching me already.

$\mathcal{P}$ART 3 - COSTA RICA

Jaslene and I met in our condo's lobby and were immediately very flirty. We took a taxi to the airport and on the way discussed everything we wanted to do on our trip. Costa Rica was actually one of the top places I wanted to visit as well; I love the outdoors and I'm pretty adventurous. Adrenaline junkies can find a lot to do on the island. But it's very hard to concentrate on Costa Rica at this point. We were both so fucking horny you could cut the sexual tension with a knife. Then she pulled an emergency adrenaline epidermal injection pen out of her bag. She said if she had an allergic reaction and couldn't breathe I would have to stab it into her thigh. She said one saved her life a few years ago when she was stung by a bee. Okay? That kind of diminished some of that sexual tension – but not for long.

I wasn't a member of the mile high club at this point in my life. I knew there would definitely be a lot of hot sex on the trip but it's pretty much impossible to do it on a jet without getting caught unless it's a private one. Someone my size barely fits in one of those airplane bathrooms solo, let alone with another person. Plus, I didn't really want to fuck with TSA in Costa Rica.

I noticed a little smirk on Jaslene's face as she looked at me and cased the plane. She wasn't going to do something crazy like drag me to the bathroom was she? If she asked me to meet her in it I certainly would have. This is the first we've seen each other in months and I assure you she was as horny as I. It was late in the morning and the plane was well lit. The stewardess was walking by and Jaslene asked her for a blanket. Jaslene covered up and started to snuggle next to me. I guess we're not heading to the bathroom. I had mixed emotions about this and my excitement passed, but not for long. Her hand started to caress my bulge. I was wearing sweatpants, as I typically do when I fly, so it was easy for her to access beneath them. I looked around nervously. We were in First Class but I don't think you can get away with sexual favors, along with the complimentary alcoholic beverage. Jaslene slithered her body up and over the large cock-blocking armrest and her mouth went down my pants.

We were luckily in the last row of First Class so no one behind could see but about three feet away to our left was an older gentlemen going to town on his computer as she went to town on me. I knew the stewardess would eventually walk by and I wasn't sure if I should pretend like nothing was happening or own it. As the stewardess approached, my reaction was to tap Jaslene and it worked. She stopped and I pretended to sleep. I opened an eye. The stewardess was gone and I tapped Jaslene again and she proceeded. She wasn't holding anything back this time. If the stewardess came back or the guy looked over, we were busted. I decided to go for it. She was giving some great fucking head. Bobbing her lips up and down with her tongue wrapped around my cock while caressing my genitals and taint. She used the right pressure and made a tight seal. Sometimes I have no clue what a girl is really doing to me and usually at this point I can't concentrate to figure it out anyways. And I explode.

I'm a huge fan of public sex and voyeurism but sure as hell don't want the charges against me for doing so. They're not minor. I'm guessing it's probably worse on a plane. But we got away with it and I must admit it was a great start to the trip. I rested and she lay on my chest watching out the window the rest of the flight. She seemed to me as if she was completely healthy so I did my best to not think about what could possibly happen to her in the near future. I was confused.

After a long drive from the airport to Jaco Beach we were a little restless, wanted to unwind and get a drink. We could tell even in the darkness how beautiful this place was. We obtained the hotel's most extravagant room which had a direct view of the ocean. One of my favorite sounds, as for most people, is the ocean. Crashing waves are one of the most peaceful and centering noises Mother Nature makes. It's also a great feeling to be in a place you have never been and everyone talks about. We were both exhilarated, dropped our bags off, and ran to the ocean. It was calling us.

After dipping our feet in to the check the water (as you must every time you visit the ocean) we were ready for a drink. A quarter mile down from our hotel we noticed lights and music playing and we decided to investigate. We ran to the bar like young children. The bar was filled with tourists and locals but everyone seemed to be having a great time in paradise. I was amazed that people were just as drunk as the ones in Vegas, but we definitely weren't in Las Vegas anymore. A sign saying "There's Magic In Paradise" caught my eye. There was a large fire on the beach that everyone was dancing around. Joyful but distorted Latin music played from the speakers.

After a few fruity tropical drinks we loosened up some and walked back down the beach. We fell and played and rolled around in the sand. I had a feeling something would go down soon so I was doing my best to not get sand everywhere. I've had some horrible beach sex. Not the best lubricant. The word sandpaper comes to mind. We started getting it on hot and heavy. We definitely missed each other and were enjoying each other's company. I picked her up off the ground, put her over my shoulder and proceeded into a little tropical jungle next to the beach. She was ready to go before her feet hit the ground and so was I. I pulled down her panties and she kicked them off along with her sandals. I turned her around. She placed her hands on a palm tree, bent over, spread her legs and stuck her ass out. What an amazing ass, tight and firm but something you could hold on to. I mounted her and went at it hard from the start. We were both very passionate people but definitely needed to knock one out of the park. And there were scary people walking all around us as well. I'm not sure if this is legal in Costa Rica or not so I'm sped it up even a little more. We continued to go at it hard. Her vagina was a perfect fit. As our bodies slapped and the sweat started dripping, Jaslene started screaming. I shushed her but don't care that much. I thought we were both cumming at the same time judging by her screams and moans but after I finished she started to say her feet burned and hurt really bad.

Were the thrusts creating friction between her feet and the ground? It's the only thing I could think of at that moment. As she put her bottoms back on and grabbed her flip flops she really started to freak out. She tells me something is wrong with her feet. I took my cell phone and used it as a flashlight to see the ground covered in ants and her feet covered in bite marks. Up and over my shoulder she goes again. I started jogging back to the hotel and I could tell she was in a lot of pain. I noticed a hose in the back of a house on the beach. I set her down next to it, turned on the water and ran it over her feet. Thankfully, it gave her some relief and we were able to laugh about it.

We started walking back to the hotel again. I was giving Jaslene a piggy back-ride this time and it didn't take too long for her feet to start hurting her again. She asked me to let her down. She hopped off of my back, undressed in the middle of the beach while smiling at me and ran to the ocean. I thought to myself, fuck it, and followed. Not caring about my clothes one bit I removed them and ran in after her.

Jaslene ran to the ocean for three reasons: to live, to stop her feet from burning, and to fuck. I love sex in the water. It's a lot less work, the extra water sensation is a total stimulant and it's fucking hot at night with waves crashing into your bodies. They were some rather large waves as well, true orgasmic waves. Some waves would hit us and send us head over feet. This time Jaslene straddled around me and pumped her body up and down mine as we made out. She soon forgot about the burning bites on her feet. I wasn't worried about anything being in the water until, I swear on my life, something, that was not her, bumped into my ass and it was not small! I think I screamed louder than she did when the ants were biting her. I think I scared an orgasm out of her. I wasn't quite there but I did still want to finish. I walked her up to where the water was about two feet deep and I finished while standing, holding her up, with her back to the ocean and one eye open.

$\mathcal{P}$ART 4 - BREATH TAKING

The next morning we woke up to the most beautiful, peaceful view I've ever seen: ocean, sun, beach, and jungle. It's almost as if our modern society hasn't recklessly tarnished this place yet. There were rather large scary-ass iguanas running around outside and wild dogs eyeing us up as we ate breakfast. I dropped some food on the ground and two of the dinosaur iguanas came flying over to get it. Holy shit! They could've totally eaten one of our feet.

I started to notice Jaslene having difficulty breathing. I didn't think she want me to notice so I pretended not to. If this was really it for her I didn't want to dwell and talk too much about her sickness. I wanted to let her live and be free, as she requested, and not have her think about her sickness. It was now becoming something I was very curious and worried about but I decided it would be best to talk about after the trip or near the end.

Our first morning consisted of surfing lessons. I promised I would teach her. We noticed a surf board rental shop across the street from our hotel. I picked out a couple longboards because they are much easier to learn on and more stable than short ones. Balancing both boards, one on each shoulder, I carried them to the beach and laid them down to show Jaslene how to stand up on the board. I showed her how to position her body so the front of the board is out of the water as well as your feet, and the board should plain across the top of the water as you paddle. And right at that moment when the waves catches your board and starts carrying you in you must position your hands on both sides of the board, jump up to your feet to a wide stance, your knees bent and put your hands out to the sides to help you balance. We attached the surf board leashes around our ankles and headed to the clear blue ocean.

I don't think she believed me when I told her how much of a workout it was to paddle against the waves to a place where you can ride one in. It kicks your butt. After you paddle out you need to take a rest before attempting to ride a wave back in but it's one of the best parts of surfing: sitting on your board a few hundred feet from shore with a magnificent view while in this vast ocean, swaying as waves pass under your board. It gives you a sense of grounding even though your feet aren't on the ground.

Once we got out a little ways she was tired, laid down on the board and caught her breath while I kept her afloat and prevented her from tipping over. I kissed her chest and ran my fingers through her hair to calm her down. Then I taught her how to sit on her board and she asked to see me ride a couple in. They weren't super big waves but I was able to catch a few. She said she wanted to save some energy so she only would try one wave and "make it count." Luckily, I was able to push her into a decent one. There she went. She rode a wave in. About ten feet into it she placed her hands as I told her to position them but was hesitant about popping up as I showed her. She decided to put one foot up and a knee on the board. She rode it in a few more feet and flipped off. It counts as surfing in my book. She loved it and she hugged, kissed, and thanked me. I was very happy this happened but in the back of my mind I couldn't help but think she wasn't going to be able to do it again. I put a half smile on my face and we headed back to land.

Next, a local guide picked us up and we headed to a crocodile safari, which was a surprise for me until we arrived. It was very exciting but it turns out crocodiles get fucking big; bigger than our boat! It was a peaceful ride over the very scary, murky water and we were lucky to see very exotic wildlife that I had never seen before. Half elephant deer things, gnarly birds, and Osama Bin Laden. Yes, Osama Bin Laden, the oldest and largest crocodile on the river. He was over 19 feet and weighed over 2,000 pounds. They called him Osama Bin Laden because they only saw him once a month. You would be gone in one bite. Jaslene really got a kick out of the whole thing. In fact, I realized she'd been smiling the entire tripe so far and that brought me a great feeling of joy.

The tour guides do not under any circumstances allow you to put any limbs outside of the boat. Unless you say you want to pet one and tip them $20. Petting a crocodile is now crossed off my bucket list.

After the safari we had lunch at a real rain forest café and stopped in a souvenir shop, where I bought us matching tribal masks. My mask is one of my favorite pieces of art and it still hangs in my living room.

I was really learning a lot about Jaslene and she fascinated me. But I was starting to get a terrifying feeling at the same time. I tried to just let it go and treat this as a normal vacation and pretend she was healthy but it was really starting to weigh on me. I was growing attached to her. I'm not sure if it was a mutual attachment. She seemed to accept her fate and wasn't worried about tomorrow and I felt horrible that I wasn't okay with it. I saw a very haunted, but nonetheless breath-taking girl and she definitely started to make me realize that every breath I took was special.

A large flock of bright red, very long, beautiful macaws flew over our heads. It was magic. She kept smiling and I wanted her to smile forever.

PART 5 - ALONE TIME

Jaslene told me she was a professional dancer, was involved in a Las Vegas act, and was still one of the girls on a billboard on the strip. She was very clean and only ate organic food, made healthy vegetable smoothies daily, and did light workouts. I was amazed how positive and wonderful a person she was with everything that had happened to her. I think most people in her position would've thrown in the towel and died in their misery in the hospital. I could tell she was a fighter. Her positivity outweighed everything else and she was the first person I can say whose flaws (she had very few) I was able to accept.

I could tell all our activities were starting to wear on Jaslene but she did her best to put on a brave face. About our fourth day in, we had plans to go to a ranch in the middle of the jungle and do a bunch of activities. I knew Jaslene was going to have difficulty but I planned on helping her along the way. When the time came she said she just couldn't do it but insisted on me going while she got a massage on the beach. I think she needed a little time to herself anyway so off I went.

The owner of the ranch was an American who was a fan of *Gigolos*. He spent a good amount of time in Orange County where he started his first business. *Gigolos* wasn't airing in Costa Rica and at this point I had forgotten about the show. It's nice to get away from the fame aspect for short periods of time. He had a bunch of questions which I gladly answered and he gave me some tips on where to get the best prostitutes while he showed me his horses. I was as polite as I could be, picked a beautiful stallion, and rode off into the jungle.

The life of a gigolo is one that I choose and will never look back on with regret. I had no idea of what I was getting into, but like everything I do, I hit the ground running. I worked my ass off my entire life. I spent four years in the Air Force, I put myself through four years of college, four years of acting school, I stripped for four years, it took me four years to get my stripping agency up running and successful and now I was starting a new chapter but was ready to settle into something and somewhere. I have moved more times than have had birthdays and with my parents separation early on in my life I have never felt I had a true home or belonging.

I always enjoyed athletics, entertaining, making people feel good, laughing, and if I could do these things and incorporate them into a profession I would be living a happy life. I'd like to think that what I do is for the greater good whether it's by making someone smile or continuing the evolution of sexual freedom since at this point in my life with my TV show, sexpert website, and sex toy line I'm pretty deep into it. With all the hard work I've done in learning about myself, what makes us who we are, the psychology of human emotion and human sexuality, it feels good to know that I am giving back, helping people and society. We have lived in some restricted fucked up times. We have come a long way but we still have a little ways to go.

It's great to have a feeling of acceptance. Originally when *Gigolos* approached me I was very hesitant. Not only had I been studying acting for the last four years of my life and knew how frowned upon an adult reality show would be in Hollywood, I was also worried about the portrayal of the adult community, professions, and the animosity from people who watched or heard about the show. I am very relieved that this is not the case at all. I had to speak up, fight, and since day one I was firm on sending a positive message if they wanted my involvement. We had to throw in some goofy shit but overall I'm happy with what we created and every season has been better than the previous.

A few months prior to my trip with Jaslene, I was in Maui hiking at the Seven Sacred Pools. At the top of the hike there was a 600 foot waterfall called Waimoku Falls. About ten of us were admiring the beauty of it. A few seconds after I took a picture of the amazing falls we heard what sounded like thunder. I looked up and the sky was filled with rocks, crashing all around us fast and hard.

Someone yelled, "RUN!" but in the confusion I couldn't figure out which way to go. They were coming down too fast. I finally got my bearings and started to run. I took two steps and rocks smashed into my shoulder, ankle, and upper thigh. I limped about twenty feet and up a hill.

A man yelled, "Is everyone okay?" At this point I was rolling around the ground in pain and wasn't able to reply. Everyone saw me and ran over. The man asked, "Did you get hit in the head?"

"I don't know," I replied. I thought I was fucked. They stood me up and I couldn't put any pressure on my foot. They carried me down the small hill but it was 1.8 miles back down to the car.

I asked for my bamboo walking stick I had made earlier and said we have to go and we have to go now. I couldn't allow it to swell up and I knew I had to go then and keep moving or I would've made the news. There was no way to get a helicopter anywhere around there and it would be insane to carry a person down this hike. It was very long, rocky, and steep. Off I went. I was taking very deep breaths to cope with the pain. Every step I took hurt more than the last. I remember screaming back at this sacred waterfall that was supposed to cleanse your spirit, "I'm fucking trying, I'm fucking trying!"

The last 1,000 feet was like the equivalent of walking 100 miles uninjured. It took every last ounce of strength I had and I collapsed in the back seat of our car. To this day I have some nasty scars by which to remember the experience. The whole event was a huge eye opener and really made me realize how precious life is.

So when my Costa Rican jungle guide stopped his horse in front of a giant waterfall, I knew this was my chance to move past almost being crushed to death by the Hawaiian waterfall. We got off our horses and the guide smacked their asses, sending them back towards the way we came. There was no way I wasn't going to repel down this waterfall. If I had lost my leg in Hawaii I would've done it with one. I had absolutely zero fear on top of the waterfall. I have repelled a few times before and trusted myself. I went down the waterfall with ease. I wished Jaslene was experiencing this with me.

After we tackled the waterfall we zip-lined back in the direction the horses ran. I wanted to attempt zip-lining upside down and once again a $20 tip allowed me to do so. I thought that was a rush until we came to another zip-line that ran hundreds of feet in the air and stretched across the entire valley. I wasn't about to do that one upside down. What a rush!

And for my favorite part of the ranch playground experience, back to my horse! I was able to have the ride of my life on the way back. I'm a fan of running horses, not just riding them. After a steady gallop I asked him if he wanted to sprint back. I think this was the first horse, out of dozens, that really enjoyed giving rides. I yelled, "Yah!" and off we went. We were sprinting and not too long after I looked back I could no longer see the guides. My hat flew off but I caught it with a lucky snag. I felt we were running at an abnormally high speed but I wasn't complaining. There was no other place I'd rather be at that moment. That was a very special ride to me that I will never forget. My mental state was changing. I don't know if it was the beauty of the Costa Rican landscape, or the haunting sexuality and life affirming energy of Jaslene. I couldn't put a finger on what has been happening to me mentally but I was living.

PART 6 - SPIRITUAL SEX

After a long exuberating conquest through a Costa Rican mountain jungle, I headed back to the hotel and found Jaslene resting in our room. I lay next to her, not wanting to disturb her but I had missed her and wanted to be close to her again. She scooted into my arms and I drifted into what felt like a meditative state. I've practiced meditation and lucid dreaming but I never had any luck finding awareness in my dreams until now. It's very hard to describe what I felt and I wasn't sure what was going on or if I was even conscious, but I felt free. Free is definitely the best word. I didn't have any stress, worries, or pain.

Jaslene drifted into the dream just as I remember her drifting in and out of my condo. I couldn't clearly make out her face but the energy from the woman in my dream was very similar to Jaslene's, it had to be her. I felt what I would describe as a spiritual state. We were floating and swirling around, or the room was swirling around. It's not what I envisioned a lucid dream to be. I didn't have complete control of what was happening but I was hyper aware. I felt more connected to the world than I ever had before and my mind had never been clearer. This was something for which I had yearned a long time.

In this dream, Jaslene spoke to me through movement and touch. Every time we communicated we were in perfect sequence. We were inside of each other in other ways than just my penis in her vagina. There wasn't a hurry. Time didn't matter. What was happening was going to forever be a part of me. There was no judgment. There was no fear. I heard the howl of an animal and turned around to see a giant wolf watching us. Jaslene peered over my shoulder and pointed at the beast, then looked into my eyes, silently telling me that this was my spiritual protector.

It's easy to forget about amazing experiences that have everlasting effects on you and go about your typical day. We are creatures of habit and that goes for our thinking processes as well. We need to disconnect from our habit and connect to something greater. We need to remember what brings true meaning to our lives and what we live for. We must take time to ourselves daily to breathe and reflect. To put it bluntly, if I learned anything from this moment it was to slow the fuck down.

I woke up to an ass rubbing on my erect cock and almost lost it immediately. I had to slow down and focus. I pulled down Jaslene's panties and while still behind her I placed my large, pulsating, almost-ready-to-explode warrior in between her legs. I used my hand to keep it pressed against her wet pussy and began to lightly slide it back and forth outside of her pussy, between her lips. Jaslene was either practicing her deep breathing exercises or getting very aroused and excited. I thought I was going to lose it before her but that wasn't the case. As she orgasmed, I put my penis inside of her and she screamed, trembled, and dug her nails into my arm. I thrust harder, deeper, and faster to finish at the same time and it didn't take much. I grabbed her breast and hair firmly and released everything that was inside of me.

Soon after, I asked if she was having a good dream when the grinding against me started but she said she didn't remember. I thought that maybe she was having a similar dream to mine, or maybe we shared that dream. To this day, I've yet to have another lucid dream.

The sun was now setting and we found ourselves walking on the beach holding hands. I felt so at peace with Jaslene. I didn't even need to hold her hand to be connected to her and I'm almost positive she felt the same. In most relationships I've encountered, I felt as if I needed to be in physical contact the majority of the time but it was different with Jaslene. I knew what we had and worries were nonexistent. Sunsets are so amazing during the golden hour of the day, showing softer and warmer colors. As the day leaves us and the jungle darkens, it stirs up panic and becomes loud from monkey howls, birds, and insects. This foreign place was spooky, but it added a little sense of adventure to our sexploration.

$\mathcal{P}$ART 7 -
OUR LAST NIGHT

It was our last night together and Jaslene kept making comments as if it were her last night ever. It really worried me but I tried to stay positive and have fun, for her sake.

The entire trip she had been saying she wanted to get drunk because it had been a long time since she had, and she wanted to get a little crazy. Up until this point I'd done a good job of steering her away from too much alcohol and focusing her on just enjoying each other and our environment. But on our last night she continued to drink and didn't want to be told not to. I felt bad because I noticed her chest pains went away when she drank but I knew it would make the complications much worse in the long run.

After having a few drinks with her I tried hard to escort her away from the hotel bar but she decided she wanted to have a couple shots. I allowed it but didn't join in. It was her decision now. I wasn't going to ruin this by starting an argument. I wasn't happy and possibly being overprotective of her so I sat in silence and people-watched.

Out of the corner of my eye, I noticed that Jaslene was giving herself a little finger action while sitting at the bar. There were plenty of people who could've noticed this. After another drink and a shot she whispered in my ear, "I was serious when I wrote you can put it anywhere...and you'd be my first. Will you teach me how?" I decided I would do my part and help her with that. Whether a girl needs surfing lessons or anal lessons, I'm here for her.

I half-carried her to the room as she stumbled up the stairs. Immediately after I opened the door she began to undress me. She slid my shorts down to my ankles and began to give me a blow job while undressing herself. After pushing me on the bed she pulled my shoes and shorts off and dropped her shorts. She spit on my dick and began to give me a hand job. I took her other hand and spit on it myself, then I moved her lubed hand behind her back and whispered to her, "Play with yourself." I could see in her face when she finally got a finger in her ass. She began sucking my cock again as she fingered her asshole. "How does it feel?" I asked her.

"It's tight." She said. "I need you to loosen me up."

She didn't have to ask twice. I grabbed her by the hair and pulled her face up to mine, kissing her passionately. "Can you get another finger in your ass?" I asked her. Her deep moan told me that yes, she could. I reached back to see what she was doing, and she had gotten three fingers inside. I looked into her eyes and nodded. She nodded back. She was ready.

She stood on both sides of me as I spit on my hand a couple times, and rubbed the saliva all over my dick. I held one of her hands and she used her other to guide me into her ass. I'm a huge fan of anal sex. It's typically much more satisfying. The anal wall is usually thicker, tighter and it gives a different sensation. It didn't take much work to get the head in. It's usually not a problem unless the woman isn't into it and tightens up. Jaslene was into it.

She sat down slowly on me, locking eyes with me, while I gently encouraged her. My dick was throbbing, pulsating, thinking about these untouched walls. Finally, she sat all the way down...and squeezed. It felt so good inside her, and her deep, heady moans were driving me over the edge. She began riding me hard. I tried to flip her over but she insisted on making me cum. Fuck, does it feel good when a girl goes to work on you. Once again, I tried to finish quickly because I didn't want Jaslene to get too worked up. I told her I was about to cum. She rode me all the way up and down my shaft. Fuck, does it feel good when a girl goes all the way down. I squeezed her tight when I unloaded. She was breathing very forcefully, loud and it sounded painful. I was really concerned. I rolled her off of me to her back and her heavy breathing stopped. I was very confused. I told her how amazing that was and she didn't respond. I listened close to her mouth to make sure she was breathing and looked for her chest to move. I saw and heard nothing. There was no response.

I freaked out and started shaking her and she came through, took a couple of shallow breaths but then stopped again. I opened her eye lids and no one was home. I shook her again and yelled, "I'm going to jab you with your pen if you don't wake up now!" Once again, a few breaths, then nothing. I shook her and smacked her in the face hard. She was barely taking breaths at this point. I ran and grabbed her purse, dumped it all over the floor and found her epi-pen. Now my heart was beating, I was shaking and freaking the fuck out. I didn't know if she was having an allergic reaction or not. She said it was for when she had a reaction and couldn't breathe. I didn't know if she was about to die or if I would possibly kill her by injecting her with the pen.

I shook her, slapped her, and yelled at her but she was half lifeless. I felt I didn't have a choice. By the time an ambulance got there she may be dead already. After reading the directions, I bit off the cap, slammed it into her thigh and pressed the top. Seconds later she woke the fuck up and asked, "What happened?"

As I explained it to her I saw her start to fade again. She thanked me and said she's supposed to go to the doctor after an injection but she's going lifeless again. I yelled at her to stay the fuck up and I will be right back. I threw on some clothes, went downstairs in panic mode and asked them to call an ambulance right away. I ran back upstairs to find her unconscious and not breathing again. Shaking and slapping didn't have any effect. I decided to give her mouth-to-mouth. It was hard to push the breaths in but it was working. I put one of my large shirts on her, I gave her a few more breaths, threw her over my shoulder and ran her to the lobby of the hotel. I didn't see or hear an ambulance but the guy assured me one was coming. I sat down on a chair with her on my lap and gave her mouth-to-mouth again.

An old piece-of-shit taxi pulls up and the driver yells to me, "Get in, let's go." He didn't speak much English and couldn't tell me how far away the hospital was. I continued to give her mouth-to-mouth for a few miles and we pulled up to a small facility I was hesitant to bring her into. I ran her inside and everyone showed a sense of urgency but couldn't communicate well. It was a nightmare. Jaslene started to wake up a little bit but was starting to have a panic attack and couldn't catch her breathe. They directed me to a treatment room, I placed her on the bed, and they asked me to leave. As I started leaving, she reached for me and said, "No!" I stopped and security attempted to grab me. I told them to back the fuck up and not to touch me again. The doctor politely asked me to leave. I decided it may be best to calm everyone down but I sure the hell didn't want her in there alone and scared. She reached for my hand. I said, very calmly, "Breathe, and I will be one foot outside of this door until you walk out of it, I promise."

I stood outside the door staring awkwardly at two security guards who I'm glad I didn't press my luck with. I was larger than them but no way in hell would I lay my hands on one.

Jaslene in the hospital and me in jail didn't sound like a good ending to this story.

After fifteen minutes, I knocked on the door. This didn't please the security guards but I needed to know what the hell was going on. The doctor came out shortly after and explained to me that she was going to be okay. She probably spoke the best English on the island but was in no way fluent. She suggested I get Jaslene to her specialist doctor as soon as possible because she had many complications and the adrenaline shot was some serious shit too. I don't think she used those specific words. Jaslene was stable, alert, and breathing okay at this point. They gave her fluids and some medicine to calm her. I lifted her to a wheelchair and the same guy was waiting outside to drive us back. He got a good tip. I carried Jaslene up to the room and tried to wrap my head around what just happened. We were on such a high before this and if I was worried for Jaslene before I was starting to lose it a little bit now. For all I knew she may pass on in her sleep. She hadn't told me everything and I had no idea what the fuck was going on. I stayed up as late as I could to watch her while throwing back some drinks after that crazy shit.

$\mathcal{P}$ART 8 - <u>GOOD BYE</u>

I thought we were both heading to the airport the next morning but I guess Jaslene had other plans. After we both packed she thanked me for saving her life and told me she would never forget me. Why would she have to use words like that!? Am I never going to see her again? Is she cutting me out of her life? She apparently decided she didn't want me to see her really sick. Was she pulling a *Point Break*, paddling off into the ocean to never return? She had told me that she would be seeking other treatment, planned on staying positive but there wasn't much doctors could do at this point. I was a little hung over, half asleep and trying to figure out what the hell just happened and what was going on.

I got in a taxi by myself and headed to the airport. Jaslene waved as the car left and I waved back, still confused as to why I was in this car while she stayed behind. *What the fuck?!*

I decided I would take the same outlook as the one I had when I decided to go on the trip and try not to over-think everything but my mind wandered. How could I not think about everything that happened? And what was going to happen to Jaslene? I didn't know whether to be sad, upset, or just happy for the time we had together. The drive was taking forever. We were going very slow, stuck behind more vehicles than I could see and there was only one lane. At this point I just wanted to get the hell out of there and I was getting really upset. I was cutting it close to the time I had to be at the airport, I had no idea where I was, and then I heard a loud pop! Fuck!

Now I was stranded on the side of a road in a beat up car with no air conditioning and a driver who doesn't speak English. I attempted to help him with the spare but he was fucking pissed off and had no problem relaying that. I kept my distance. I noticed he had a very beat up jack and wrench, not a crowbar, to fix the flat. After much yelling, banging, and frustration I watched the wrench go flying into a river. I had a few choices at this point and one involved throwing the little angry Costa Rican in the river after it but instead I decided to attempt to flag down drivers. I started to get some dirty and scary looks so I let the little angry Costa Rican take over after he cooled off a little bit. I hid in the car. Luckily someone finally stopped and had a crowbar that worked on the tire but now I had no chance of catching my flight.

PART 9 - MEANINGLESS

I wasn't able to catch a flight until the next day. I just wanted to rest. I remembered the name of the hotel where the owner of the ranch said the best prostitutes were so I figured it would be a decent hotel. Nope. After switching my first room because it was near the music and the walls were paper-thin and switching my second room because someone hot boxed it with cigar smoke, I found myself in a room debating if I would be better off sleeping in the alley. I couldn't help wondering how many guys have gotten off with a Costa Rican prostitute on that bed. Not a great image.

I laid down after throwing the top blanket on the floor. Once I hit the bed my eyes were wide open and I realized I wouldn't be sleeping anytime soon, if ever, especially on that squeaky piece of shit mattress. What to do? *Let's go talk to some Costa Rican prostitutes*, I thought to myself. I needed to clear my fucking mind, or so I thought. I walked through a casino and had a seat at the main bar. I was blown away by all of the girls standing on the outside of the bar and staring. There were about 30 girls, about two other guys, and me. It was semi-mentally damaging at first until I met a guy named Charlie.

Charlie was a Costa Rican entrepreneur; he said he did something involving tourists. I don't quite remember, I was paying attention to all the hot Costa Rican ass circled around me. I explained to Charlie that it's quite different in American strip clubs. The girls in America are too damn aggressive and pushy. I've still yet to have one Costa Rican come up to me. The Costa Ricans wouldn't survive for long in the states. He didn't really have an explanation. I guess it might be common courtesy.

Costa Rica's prostitutes are definitely not afraid of eye contact and I'm not sure if Costa Rican prostitutes blink. Charlie explained to me that the good ones are $100 American for an hour and you can get some down to $20. Prostitution is legal in Costa Rica, and the girls have to get tested and carry special cards to work in the hotel. Holy shit! I had actually never picked up a prostitute before. Or I should say, paid for one. This might have been a first. It was definitely on top of my bucket list, even above zip lining. I thought paying for company would be pretty dope. Charlie picked one out, waved at her and she seemingly teleported to the stool next to him. I was thinking to myself that this really wasn't all that bad. Most of these girls were 8's and up. And then, of course, the one blonde, Dominga, caught my eye.

It turns out Costa Rican prostitutes aren't the best conversationalists but I wanted to get to know one a little before…getting to know one…I felt it was necessary to have a conversation with her. Women in general fascinate me, not to mention their motives. Here's what I found out: she's not a natural blonde. She only dyes her hair to get noticed (I guess it worked). And she became a prostitute to take care of her kids. That's about it. I was really starting to miss Jaslene. Charlie said he was going to go have some fun and left with a girl. I decided I was going to try to do the same. Up to the room we went.

I kicked off my shoes and laid down. She removed her clothes quickly. She was definitely very comfortable in the nude. I wasn't turned on as much as the last time a girl did this in front of me.

She approached the bed and I thought it might be a good idea to rinse off before. I got up, grabbed her hand and lead her into the bathroom. I caressed her from behind grabbing her ass and tits. We both dried off and went to the bed.

Dominga went right to town on my cock. What do you know? A deep-throater. That is definitely a talent when a girl can do that to me. This helped me get through it. I wasn't sure, until that happened, if I was going to or not. I couldn't stop thinking about Jaslene and wishing I was with her, grabbing her tits and ass. I actually tried to finish and was close but she started coming up. I got up and ran to the bathroom to grab a condom. I slapped that baby on, laid back down, and Dominga jumped right on. It was a very tight fit. Luckily, she was wet and she slid right down. As I was being ridden I was just thinking to myself how much better it was with Jaslene. Going from a life-changing sexual experience with a possible soul mate to someone you have no connection with whatsoever isn't anything great.

I started to get upset with myself. In fact, I was getting furious. How could I go from what I had with Jaslene to this emptiness? I just wanted Dominga to leave. I stood up with her legs wrapped around me as she held on. I spun her facing away from me and against a wall. I wrapped my arm around her stomach, put one hand on the back of her neck and forcefully finished. I paid her, thinking that she would go but she wanted to stay. She told me I didn't have to pay for her company anymore and insisted. I told her, sorry, but I had a really long trip and needed to rest. I thanked her and had to walk her out. This only made me feel worse and made me realize more what I was now missing. I felt an evil building inside of me. Anger, which hasn't been a part of my life for some time, was the only emotion breaking the surface. I had to get out of Costa Rica as soon as possible.

$\mathcal{P}$ART 10 - LIFE LESSON

I definitely left a part of me in Costa Rica but I took home something as well. Jaslene was a very strong, positive, and healthy person that I became an erudite life student of. She not only taught me the value of life but the value of myself and of each moment. We don't know how much time we have and life is way too short. I know, it's a cliché, but clichés exist for a reason, and Jaslene changed my life when she taught me this. I learned more than ever how delicate and precious life is.

I'm still confused about whether we had found love or just great chemistry. Time, staying busy, and habit is what saved me from depression when I returned. Luckily I became extremely busy with the filming of *Gigolos*, my sex toy line, appearances, clients, expanding my company – Explicit Strippers – to Las Vegas, my sexpert website, my music, my dogs, buying a house, and training. Thank God. My time with Jaslene was so emotionally overwhelming it could have been crippling. I did take time to myself but it was hard to think about the good that came from this without being so sad. Writing about all of this stirs up some strong inner emotions again. But I am glad I was able to go back over this sexploration adventure and take you with me. Thanks for coming along for the ride.

It's sad it sometimes takes the fear of death to live. I thank Jaslene for sharing possibly the last precious time she had left with me. It was an honor and a lesson. I was in the process of becoming a better person and this undoubtedly helped my expedition. She hasn't replied to my texts thanking her and wishing her the best. I do hope and pray for a letter. If it comes to me in an email or a dream, but at least I'm able to close my eyes and be in Costa Rica with Jaslene whenever I need to get away.

DEDICATED TO JASLENE

BRADLEY LORDS

$\mathcal{F}$ORBIDDEN FRUIT

I remember the very first time I looked upon her. It was a Friday afternoon, the week was just winding down. She came by the office to give my boss, John, some things he needed for his weekend trip. It was as if the office gained an entirely different energy about it when she graced it with her presence. I swear I could match her sweet smell to the tapping of her high heels every time. Although we had spoken several times in passing and at small gatherings, it was the looks absorbed through our eyes where the real intensity was. Jane was not the most incredibly gorgeous woman I had ever seen nor the sexiest, but it was just something about her overall package that made her so appealing and somewhat irresistible. Her hair waved through the air like soft silk dancing in the wind. She had the brightest and sharpest eyes that could pierce the most confident of men. I couldn't quite figure out why she was so enticing to me. Was it her tiny stature and young fresh skin or was it that sweet smell and those exotic eyes? I thought to myself though, perhaps it was the simple fact she was my bosses wife and I was not suppose to have her...

A year or so had gone by and I hadn't seen Jane nor John really too much either. I had since went to work on my own with my private fitness centers and other businesses. I did see John in the gym from time to time and once in a while we would go grab lunch or a drink. Then came this cool summer night. It was a very average easygoing night as most Thursdays are. I was just relaxing at home after a long day, checking out some shows on television and doing a little work on the computer. The text I received was a tad bit surprising but not extremely out of the ordinary. I simply assumed she was out with friends again and most likely putting a few drinks down. After all, Jane was the younger party type girl who always looked for a wild night of dancing and partying anytime the opportunity presented itself. Once I read a few of the texts it was apparent she was inquiring where I was and what my plans where for the late evening. I was a little uncertain why she would text so late and actually care what I was up to this late but then I figured it was just a late drunk flirty kind of text. I know we had always looked upon one another in a certain intimate kind of way. There was no denying we were attracted to one another by the look in her eyes while looking into mine and I'm certain my eyes could give away at least a bit of the attraction I had for her. She then went on to explain where she was and that she might be in need of a ride home. I asked her if she was ok and if she wanted me to call someone for her or send a cab. I decided to go on and give her a call and get to the point of it all instead of baffling myself with all of these uncertain and somewhat confusing texts. Once I heard her voice it was obvious just how much she had to drink. Her voice was still so sweet and sexy, the innocent young soft voice that seems to make you want to just squeeze that person tight and feel their body as they spoke. I had to admit, that kind of voice and especially hers, did make me feel a special excitement inside of me. I asked her what all was happening and why she had decided to contact me this late in the evening. She then went on to tell me how she was out with the girls and it was a small party for one of them who just split with her husband. That alone told me it was a group of wild women up to no good.

I wanted to explain to her that I could call her a cab where she was or help direct her into the right direction, but it was almost as if I just truly could not help myself. Her voice was so enticing and the picture I was drawing in my head of her in a cute little dress with high heels was killing me. I could almost even smell her sweet smell and already feel her soft brown skin in the palm of my hand and into my fingertips. My mind, along with certain other parts of my anatomy, was at this point racing wild and causing my body temperature to heat while I sat there holding my phone eyes closed. Should I give in? Should I be the naughty boy I so much want to be? Or should I take the more ethical route and do my best to assist her in this time of need by being the friend who helps another friend. What would the right thing be to do? I was quite torn at just how bad this had me excited and a bit crazy I was even contemplating going to get her. I finally had enough and said "yes" I will go and pick you up. She was so excited, almost like you told someone over the phone they just won a new car. I somehow managed to talk myself into it by believing she would surely be in some kind of danger if I didn't run to her aid immediately. I told myself it would be horrible of me to leave a friend in need out in the late night without a car or shelter. She was a bit intoxicated after all so it was one hundred percent the right moral thing to do. Well, I was most likely stretching the moral part of it a small amount I suppose but who doesn't from time to time?

I threw some casual clothes on and jumped into my car to head off to pick her up. The twenty-minute drive felt like three hours. All I could think of was how she is dressed and who is there with her and would see the two of us together. She called again when I was about five minutes away and told me she was now at the Denny's alone, her friend who she had been with already left. I was a little relieved in that she would be alone and no one would see the two of us together but at the same time the good person inside me was also worried because she was now at a restaurant so late at night all by herself. I pulled into the parking lot and then there she was walking out the door. Those silky brown legs easing out of this blue tight little dress. The dress was so high you could imagine seeing her bend over directly in front of you. The high heels were approximately four to five inches with sparkling bright toes glistening out of them in the ends. The top of the dress dipped down just subtle enough to make out her brown cleavage from the sexy tight black bra pushing her breasts up and in to the perfect form. Every bit of the one hundred and ten pounds of her swayed in a innocent yet mischievous way as she walked toward my car. She had the most gorgeous long thick jet-black hair I had ever seen. Her hair was most definitely something out of a salon commercial. I wanted to run my fingers through it and squeeze it in my clinched fists. Her eyes were probably the best part which is quite hard to imagine with everything she had going on. They had this certain slant to them as if she were mixed with all the right ethnic races. I proceeded to get out of the car and walk over to her and open the car door to let her in. She walked up and gave me a big hug before I could even get the" hello how are you" out of my mouth. Oh my god she smelled so damn good. I had only been this close to her maybe once or twice when saying hello or a casual hug whenever we saw one another. I wanted to almost squeeze her in even tighter and feel her body on mine. The nicer guy inside of me refrained from it however, and I asked if everything was going ok and if she was ready to go.

I let her into the car, watching her shiny sexy oh so tan slender legs glide in after she sat down. The breeze blew her hair just right as the door opened and shut. As I walked around to get into the driver side my mind was racing as to where she expected me to take her and if was a good idea to be out with her this late especially after she had obviously been drinking all night long. I climbed on into the car myself and buckled in. I asked where she wanted to be taken to and her reply was a very mischievous, " where ever you would like to take me." I thought to myself very extremely naughty places and scenes but instead simply replied, "should I just take you to your house?". That of course was not remotely what she wanted to hear I could tell. She then started to give the hints it would be better if we went to my place for a bit so she could sober up and relax some from the long night. I agreed to it almost immediately as if it weren't really even my choice.

My mind definitely wanted that outcome and I was certain my body wanted it even more. I wanted to run my hand all up and down those gorgeous legs and feel how incredibly soft they actually were. Her smell of sweet lotions and products conquered with a perfect subtlety, any scents my car might have had. I felt myself going into a sort of trance of inner eroticism and desire. How bad did she also want it I asked myself? Was she also feeling this tension there coming from each of us? Without being able to help myself, I informed her that if she felt tired or nauseous, she was welcome to lay the seat back or she could also lie in my lap if that was better. She smiled and blushed a tiny bit as I gave her a slight smirk when I said it and replied to it with how that might be a great idea in the very, very near future. I wanted her so bad at this point but didn't want it to be too obvious.

We finally arrived back to my place after a drive which seemed to last an eternity. As I helped her out of the car and into the house I could tell she was quite tipsy by the way she swayed around and held on to me at every account. It could have been she only wanted to have a reason to grab onto me as well, which I had to admit I wanted her to do. I had a roommate at the time so we attempted to not be too loud and wake him. That of course was easier said than done with her heels clanging and knocking into things in the dark. I showed her into my bedroom and laid her down so she could rest. I told her if she got cold easily then not to worry because I gave off a large amount of body heat. That was exactly what she wanted to hear. She snuggled up right next to me and began rubbing her chilly soft nose against my neck then her soft juicy thick lips starting kissing around my neck and jaw line. It felt so good I wanted to strip down right away. I had to ask myself if this was ok to do. Was this what she really wanted? Was it going to have severe consequences later? What would happen if anyone we knew found out, especially if it got back to John. What would his reaction be? John was not only my boss but also a very powerful guy. She felt so good at this point I honestly started not to give a shit at all. I drifted into this crazy sexual mood and state of mind. I took my hand from the lower of her back and down across her curvy tight little ass and right onto those silky soft legs. They felt even better than I could have possibly imagined. I grasped her upper thigh tightly and pulled her leg across the top of me. I kissed those luscious lips with their sweet taste. I used my lips to pull on her bottom lip so I may take it in between mine and rub my tongue in circles all over her bottom lip. She tasted so good I thought, as I wondered how her other set of lips were going to taste. I placed her petite hands onto my chest and with my much larger hands on top of hers she massaged it and played with the short hair upon it and lowered her head so she could work her mouth to there as well. She began nibbling on my pecs and took her tongue down the center dip of my abs. Her mouth felt so amazing as it kissed me all around my abs and down my obliques. Her tiny little hand placed itself onto my crotch which had grown exponentially larger by this time. She peeked up at me with those seductive big brown beautiful eyes and said "oh my" as she squeezed the shaft of my fat cock in her hand. She was quite impressed with the size of it and became more aroused. The next devious remark of, "we are just so naughty aren't we?" made her eyes glisten with this unique sense of desire and deep enthusiasm. She then smiled like a mischievous child up to no good and returned to the adventure she had begun with her mouth.

I took both of my hands and ran her thick black hair through my fingers as I caressed the side of her head. She nibbled a little more around my obliques and upper thighs until making her soft lips lower and onto the bottom of my shaft. She licked it from bottom to top and then gave peck kisses all over each side of it. As she paced both hands around it there was still plenty more sticking out which she enthusiastically kissed and licked on. Her lips seemed to become more succulent and soft as they embraced all of my cock into her mouth and throat. I was so turned on and hard at this point I wanted to explode. There was no way of course I was going to allow that to happen without first tasting her and feeling my hard cock inside of her. I then pulled her head up to my lips and kissed her again while rolling her over to her back. I made my way to her neck and ears first, flicking the tip of my tongue a little on her cute tiny earlobes. I exhaled then sucked it with a wide-open mouth on her ear to bring a cool sensation to it. The goose bumps raised on her arm as she giggled some. I took it to her shoulder next and bit on it some, just the right amount to where it didn't hurt her but to where she could definitely feel a bit of sting. She enjoyed the nibbling and so I kept working my way down further and further. I had to of course stop on her sexy belly button ring. I bit onto it and used my tongue to rattle it around my teeth. I worked my hands onto her waist and squeezed downward to up under her ass. I pulled my hands even lower until they were grasping the back of her thighs and started to lick on and nibble on those smooth quads and inner thighs. I pushed my hands back up again but this time under that tight dress she still had on. I positioned each ass cheek into the palms of my hands as I took my tongue up and down each side of her panty line. I licked up the left side of her panties then trickled the back of my tongue back downward slowly then upward a little faster than the downward glide. I did this several times on both sides of her panties next to her sweet smelling vagina. I knew it was driving her crazy by not only the sounds she was making but also the feel of her fingertips and nails digging into my head. I brought one hand around to the front from over the top of her crotch and slipped my index and middle finger into the inner side of her panties and pulled them over some. I opened my mouth wide and breathed in as I placed my lips onto the side of her vagina and closed them slowly while slightly sucking on it just enough to pull the skin very gently out. She began to quiver a little as I sucked a tiny bit stronger each time. I repeated this several times from both sides before taking my hands back up under her ass and slipping my fingertips into the back upper part of her panties.

I began to gently pull the panties down while I kissed her in various sporadic locations all around her thighs and crotch area. Once the panties were gone I replaced my hands under her again and grasped her ass firmly. I stuck my tongue far out so that the back rough part would be exposed and gently rubbed it from the bottom of her vagina all the way to the top. I then took the middle of my tongue and placed it on the hood covering the clitoris while folding the edges to slightly touch the edges next to the clitoris. I proceeded to vibrate my tongue side to side.

Her soft little voice was almost whimpering with excitement as I felt her legs quivering on the sides of my head. The idea still in my head telling me this was not the right thing to be doing seemed to only intensify the feelings of passion and desire. I could tell from her body she also was feeling the overwhelming eroticism between our bodies. These thoughts racing through my head of who may know or who could know, or what if someone already knows, made the intensity even higher and only fueled this hot steamy passion we were both falling so victim to. I loved the sweet taste she had and wanted to make her orgasm over and over again, which I did. Her thighs squeezed my head tight as she dug her nails into the top of my head. She was up to at least three decent orgasms by now and it was time to connect our bodies to the full extent. I ran my tongue up her crotch and across her abdominals. I of course had to stop by the nipples for a brief while to show them the attention they surely deserved. Such cute small round brown nipples. They contrasted perfectly with her morena skin tone. I pulled at them with my lips squeezed firmly together. I also opened my mouth wider and sucked in a little to give my quick tongue some room to flick around and take the now hard nipple from side to side and up and down. After both nipples had their equal share of playtime, I progressed further north until reaching the neck once again. I bit on it hard in some places and soft in others. I kissed softly on her ears and whispered to her, "How do you feel?" She could hardly breathe it seemed and was gasping for her deep energy to get back to her real world conscious senses to say to me, "Oh my god its more incredible than I've imagined, I can't believe we're doing this". I told her I felt the same on both accounts as well. This naughtiness was in such an enormous way amplifying the already hot and steamy fire and attraction we had between us. I kissed her soft lips and we nibbled on one another more and more as I positioned my body above hers until we almost effortlessly joined ourselves together.

Even with her so dripping wet, the fit of my cock inside of her was extremely firm and tight. She let out a sputtering exhale as I let it go deeper inside of her. I moved into a steady flowing motion to allow my cock to go just deep enough to scrape the cervix but not to hit it too hard as to make her resist, at least not yet. Our bodies flowed and danced together as the hot passion and temperature rose to insane levels. We rolled over so she could have some freedom to move that athletic slim firm body all over the top of my body. I held her by her tight little waist and waved my hands in a motion as if I was splashing water onto myself. It allowed for her body to get the full impact of my cock deep inside of her hitting the front, back, and middle of her insides. She could sense I was growing closer to my climax and said to tell her when I'm almost ready. "You feel so good inside of me, I don't want to stop yet." I told her I would keep holding back and allow my cock to grow even harder and pulsate inside of her until she could feel the vibrations inside of her. As I got right up to that moment I grasped her sides tightly and said, "Are you ready?" She went directly down to my pulsating cock and wrapped her steamy soft fat lips around it and took every drop of my cum into her mouth. She appeared to enjoy it as someone would take in their favorite ice cream. She fell down beside me as we both lay catching our breath, and our senses. I couldn't believe we had done this but still because it had felt so fucking amazing, I knew in my head I would had done the exact same thing if given the chance again. I asked her if she had any regrets and she said none whatsoever. Me neither I said. It was the most intense and passionate sex I had experienced in quite some time. I had plenty of gorgeous and experienced women in my time but the special circumstances of this situation had most definitely given it the extra fire in it. I wondered if all the naughty or forbidden erotic experiences would always be this intense and incredible. Was it actually forbidden though? Was the wife of my boss and long-term friend always off limits?

Several days had gone by and there was no other random texts or calls. Was she a bit embarrassed or filled with guilt from our hot rendezvous?

I did, however, run into John shortly after my encounter with his wife. That was a trip. When he reached out to shake my hand, all I could think was, *Does he know where this hand has been? Does he know what this hand has done to his wife?* He obviously didn't, because I'm still here to tell this story. I felt bad as I talked to him, but it was worth it.

As my mind ponders across all of these vast recollections of sexual experiences, I find myself most intrigued by the scenarios as to where the premise of the occurrence was heavily based upon such an inappropriate or unethical behavior, according to society, a forbidden fruit perhaps. Countless wives, girlfriends, colleagues, housekeepers, nanny's, flight attendants, professors, maids, bosses, the list is amazingly elaborate. A business partners wife in the front seat of my truck, the cute maid cleaning my room in the hotel, the hand job by the flight attendant in the back galley, the list goes on. This concept burned into our brain by society "you're not supposed to do that", makes it the ever more appealing and rewarding it seems. The old proverb of how the grass is always greener on the other side, could not apply more than it does in eroticism and sexual fantasy. So why is it we want so passionately want we are not suppose to have? Why does breaking the 'rules' make the experience so much more fulfilling? I wish to expand and recall some of my sexual experiences tapping into this realm of taboo and intrigue. Is this what true passion and desires are made of? Can it really be true that the most sought after and erotic pleasures in this life, honestly be the forbidden fruit of mankind?

Made in the USA
Middletown, DE
09 April 2017